Deep D
There Are Still ivlermaids

PENNY GAY

ISBN: 0-9552740-0-1
ISBN 13 Digit: 978-0-9552740-0-8

Printed and bound in Great Britain by
Headland Printers,
Bread Street, Penzance, Cornwall TR18 2EQ

Penny Gay
44 Carn Bosavern
St Just-in-Penwith
TR19 7QX

For Paul and Ruth Jenkins

Hillside Farm

Bryher

THE ISLES of SCILLY

INTRODUCTION

In 1949 my father painted a watercolour picture of a thatched cottage on Bryher in the Isles of Scilly. Known as Clem's cottage, that little house has been part of my life for over fifty years and I have always been curious to find out more about the little old lady who lived there. Her name was Clementina Hicks and she was born on Bryher in 1868.

After she died in 1953, the cottage was pulled down. Now only the ruins of her hearth and home are left, together with the sycamore tree which she planted near the front porch. There are people living on Scilly now who remember Old Clem and her cottage. She seems to have been quite a character.

Two years ago, I began researching Clemmie's family history. I then looked at it within the context of what was happening on Scilly during the early half of her life. The overall picture which came to light inspired me to write this book.

'Deep Down There Are Still Mermaids' is a fictitious story about young Clemmie growing up, but it is almost entirely based on fact. It describes real people and places and is set against a background of actual events which took place on Scilly, on the island of Bryher in particular, almost a hundred years or more ago. The account of Clemmie's family and upbringing is fundamentally accurate. However, in order to bring the characters to life, some incidents and conversations are imaginary. These have been prompted by my own thoughts and experiences during a lifetime of holidays on the islands.

Many anecdotal details have been passed on to me by people who knew Clem as a very old lady and most of these have been included in the book. From what I have read and also been told, I believe that, in essence, the final outcome of the story is almost certainly true. When you have finished reading it, I think you may well agree that truth is often stranger than fiction.

Penny Gay 2005

CLEMENTINA HICKS

1868 - 1953

CLEMMIE'S FAMILY TREE

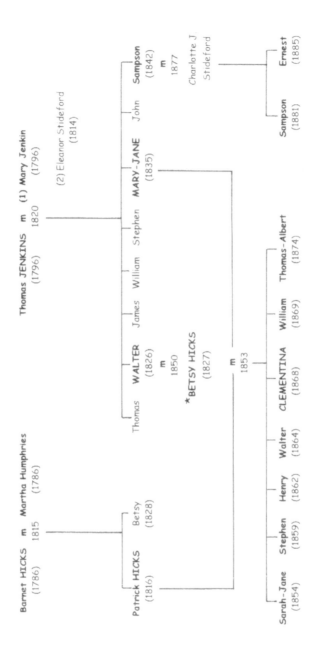

Barnet HICKS m Martha Humphries
(1786)   1815   (1786)

Thomas JENKINS m (1) Mary Jenkin
(1796)   1820   (1796)

(2) Eleanor Stideford
(1814)

Patrick HICKS
(1816)

Betsy
(1828)

Thomas

WALTER
(1826)
m
1850

*BETSY HICKS
(1827)

James

William

Stephen

MARY-JANE
(1835)

John

Sampson
(1842)
m
1877

Charlotte J
Stideford

m
1853

Sampson
(1881)

Ernest
(1885)

Sarah-Jane
(1854)

Stephen
(1859)

Henry
(1862)

Walter
(1864)

CLEMENTINA
(1868)

William
(1869)

Thomas-Albert
(1874)

*BETSY HICKS
Daughter of Richard & Elizabeth HICKS

CHAPTER ONE

'Oh my darlin' Clementine . . .'

Clementina Hicks was just a small baby when her parents gave her away. There was never any secret about it. How could you keep a secret like that on a little island like Bryher? Clemmie loved her own family and hardly a day went by when she did not see them. However, she always lived with her Uncle Walter Jenkins and his wife, Betsy.

Of course, she couldn't remember the day she was christened at the granite font in Bryher Church, but Uncle Walter often told her about it.

'That was the day you came to us, Clemmie. It was such a wonderful moment for Betsy and me - but it was so sad for your mother.'

March 10th 1868 - Uncle Walter never forgot that day. It was as important to him as Clemmie's birthday.

Everyone had crowded into the little Church right beside the beach.

'You didn't cry,' Uncle Walter said. *'You were never one to show your feelings, Clemmie - always a strong little character in your own strange way.'*

There would be several times in her life when she needed that strength.

'After you were named, we all came out of the Church into the early spring sunshine. I didn't really enjoy christenings. Your Aunt Betsy and I had been married for nearly twenty years and never had a baby of our own. So while everyone clustered round to fuss over you, I stood back and waited and your aunt stayed right beside me. She knew how I felt. Suddenly everyone was stepping away, as your mother walked towards us with you in her arms. She was smiling through her tears.

"You take her, Walter. You and Betsy can take care of her for us. Patrick and I already have four mouths to feed."

You were thrust into my arms before either your aunt or I could even think, let alone speak. By the time we were ready to protest, your mother was climbing the curving path to the top of the hill. That was the bravest and kindest thing any woman can do. Don't ever think badly of your mother.'

And Clemmie never did.

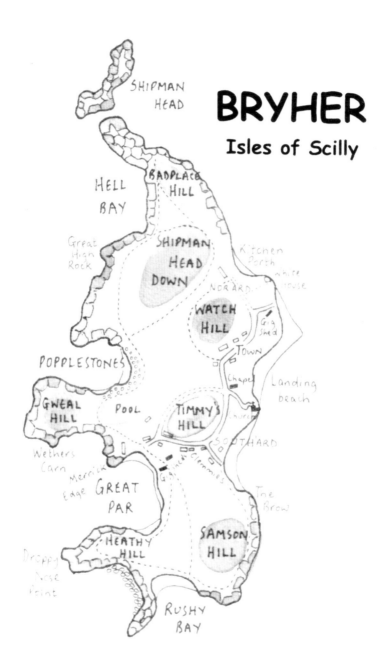

BRYHER

Isles of Scilly

SHIPMAN HEAD

HELL BAY

BADPLACE HILL

Great High Rock

SHIPMAN HEAD DOWN

Kitchen Porth

White House

NORARD

WATCH HILL

Gig Shed

POPPLESTONES

TOWN

Chapel

Landing Beach

GWEAL HILL

POOL

TIMMY'S HILL

Church

SOUTHARD

Wethers Carn

Merrick Edge

GREAT PAR

Grannies Clemmies

The Brow

HEATHY HILL

SAMSON HILL

Droppy Nose Point

RUSHY BAY

CHAPTER TWO

'Oh! it's a snug little Island . . .'

Clemmie loved Bryher. It was the pricking of tears in her eyes, the lump in her throat, the joy in her heart and the golden thread of happiness running through her life. True, she didn't show her feelings. She had to be tough, but she knew that this inner strength was drawn from the deep sense of contentment that came from living in such a magical place.

She could roam on Bryher a thousand times and every moment would bring something new. From Samson Hill in the south to Shipman Head in the north, she knew and loved every inch of the island in all seasons and weathers: the neat pincushions of pink thrift; shaggy flowers peeping between the claw-like leaves of Hottentot fig; towering spires of foxgloves; golden gorse, glorious even on the dullest day; the purple heather and rust-red bracken of autumn; toadstools gleaming in the dewy grass of early morning; the sweet, sharp taste of ripe blackberries picked in September; the peculiar scent of camomile or samphire; the tang of salty sea mingled with wet seaweed; a cuckoo's haunting call; the jubilant song of the thrush; raucous seabirds; an inquisitive seal; strutting oystercatchers; swans gliding across the Pool - a tiny land of countless delights, edged with granite rocks and white beaches and washed by the ever-changing sea.

On a low spring tide you can walk from Bryher across to Tresco. The channel becomes a wet-smooth stretch of sand, squiggled with worm casts and strewn with tangled clumps of seaweed. When the sea comes in, it is rarely more than choppy. Seen from the top of Watch Hill on a calm day, the water has a satiny sheen - sometimes pearly grey, but more often a sparkling deep blue, shot with green. On a still moonlit night it shines like polished glass. Can this be the same sea as the one that roars between the Norrard Rocks and pounds into Hell Bay, turning it into a raging tumult, a boiling cauldron of crashing waves and spray? You would not think so, yet you can see both in less than half an hour, just by walking from one side of Bryher to the other.

It's a little world of its own, ruled by tides and at the mercy of all winds and weathers. Clemmie couldn't begin to explain how she felt about this little patch of heaven. In winter it could be wild and bleak, but to her it was always beautiful. She never knew or wanted any other life than this.

CHAPTER THREE

Bryher – island of hills

It hardly seems possible that there could be room for six hills on a little island less than a mile and a half long and only half a mile wide, so it's surprising to find exactly that number of places all named as hills on a map of Bryher. In addition, Shipman Head Down, though not officially called a hill, has always counted as one. Spread over a large area, these would be nothing but small hillocks, but in this miniature landscape they are definitely hills, topped by outcrops of granite and joined by curving dips and hollows. Paths and tracks wind everywhere - between, around, up and down - and at every twist and turn, at every level, there are fleeting glimpses, then vast, open views of sky, sea, rocks and the gentle outline of low-lying green islands fringed with white beaches.

However, it is not just the hills and hollows that give Bryher its special quality. You can walk round the island in less than two hours and in that time see such a variety of scenery, you would never believe! On the east side, sheltered from the wider ocean by Tresco and St. Martin's beyond, flower fields slope down towards the shore. A long stretch of beach shelves gently to the water's edge, reaching out to the sandbanks in mid-channel as the tide ebbs.

It usually takes a shipwreck to draw Bryher folk to the north end of the island and Clemmie didn't often venture that far. Up there, is a huge expanse of springy peat and heather, weathered into ripples and furrows and criss-crossed by rough tracks and ancient boulder walls. On the hillside around Hell Bay there are burial chambers and the remains of an Iron Age fort. Sometimes, even on a warm day, you feel yourself shiver. If you look towards Shipman Head when a strong Atlantic breeze is blowing, the contrast between east and west is clear. To your right are high outcrops of granite with a sheer drop in many places to the deep, calm water of the channel. On the other side, the turf slopes more gently down to the rugged shores of Hell Bay, so that it is quite possible to walk near the edge, feel the spray and hear the menacing roar of the waves as they crash against the rocks. In late spring, the grassy dip between Shipman Head Down and Badplace Hill is covered with drifts of thrift, each rounded tump thick with clusters of dancing sea pinks. Here, too, in the cliff near Great High Rock, is a spring of fresh water, so shaded by overhanging granite that the sun never shines on it. There is an old superstition on Bryher that the water from this spring will cure wounds and sores.

On one of their fishing trips, Uncle Walter showed Clemmie the gulf between Bryher and Shipman Head. It was just wide enough for a small boat to squeeze through at high tide on a calm day, but could be crossed on foot when the tide was low. He also pointed out the granite profile that gave the headland its name. Clemmie never dared to climb right to the end of Bryher, but she knew that her brothers used to scramble about on the rocks there and even went across the gap. It wasn't easy, because the sides of the chasm were very steep. They looked as though they had been torn apart rather than worn away by the washing of the tide.

Although Hell Bay was wild and exciting, Clemmie's favourite part of the island was the peaceful, grassy stretch of land from Popplestones round to Rushy Bay. She always thought that Popplestones was such a good name. It seemed to describe perfectly the rounded pebbles and boulders heaped high along the top of the beach, which crunched and rattled as she walked on them.

On this side of Bryher, it was as if the Atlantic, like some huge sea monster, had taken great bites out of the coastline to make sheltered bays and beaches. She could hear the roar of the ocean in the Norrard rocks and sometimes the seas were so rough that the spray broke over and into the Pool. Yet on quiet days, Popplestones and Great Par would be still and calm, each cradled in its own encircling ring of rocks. In this low-lying landscape, three hills - Gweal, Samson and Heathy (more a hummock than a hill) - seemed to stand like sentinels, as if especially put there to protect the entire stretch of grass and sand between them. To Clemmie, it was a haven of peace and whenever she was there she felt that all was right as right could be.

CHAPTER FOUR

Sparrow Cottage

When Clemmie was a child there were about twenty-five houses on Bryher, with just over a hundred people living in them. The simple cottages huddled together between the hills, close to land that had been cleared for farming. Each group of houses had at least one well of water nearby. There was a cluster of dwellings on the southern slopes below Watch Hill, known optimistically as the Town, and another group to the south of Timmy's Hill called Southard. This was where Clemmie lived with her aunt and uncle - Sparrow Cottage some people called it. A number of houses were scattered around Pool and one row stood, very exposed, close to the Atlantic shore at Merrick Edge. Perhaps even more isolated were the few families living up at Norrard, in the cottages overlooking Kitchen Porth and in the White House, with its fine view of Cromwell's Castle - a round granite tower on the Tresco side of New Grimsby Channel.

Some of the cottages were two up, two down, with roofs of grouted slates, but Sparrow Cottage was long and low with a chimney at each end. The roof was covered with a layer of thatch made out of reeds from Tresco Pool. It overhung the cottage walls and was held down by a network of straw ropes pegged into the granite below the eaves and gables.

Uncle Walter used to tell Clemmie how the straw ropes were spun on St. Mary's using a throw-crook, which was a curved piece of wood with a hook in the middle, over which a handful of dampened straw was doubled. The spinning needed two people. One - usually a bare-footed boy or girl - turned the throw-crook, walking slowly backwards from the spinner, who held the other end of the straw in one hand and fed fresh handfuls through his fingers with the other. In this way, each new bundle was taken up and twisted. When it grew too long to manage, the twisted rope was unhooked and coiled into a cocoon-shaped ball. The boy or girl moved forward, the end of the rope was then hitched over the hook again and the turning began once more. In this way it was possible to make long lengths of straw rope.

The cottage backed onto the road, but sat a bit below it. Between the road and the house there was a deep ditch, running the full length of the north wall. This stopped the water from Timmy's Hill soaking straight into the granite. A path led down the east side of the cottage, through a little gate and there you were.

The front of the cottage faced south and had two small sash windows painted green, with four square panes in each window. There was a little porch in the middle and the door was on the east side of the porch. The view from there was wonderful. A valley stretched from the east side of Bryher to the west and fields sloped down from the cottage and Hillside, as far as the foot of Samson Hill. To the south-east were glimpses of the boats plying their way up and down the channel between Bryher and Tresco. On a sunny day, the sand of Tresco's Appletree Bay glistened white against the deep blues and greens of the sea. Samson Hill was due south and so near it seemed to tower to a great height, though it was really nothing to walk to the top of it. To the south-west were the grassy fringes of Rushy Bay, the gentle rise of Heathy Hill and beyond that the great Atlantic. Through a small dip in the landscape, the distant tower of the Bishop Rock Lighthouse was just visible on the horizon.

There weren't many people who did not stop to enjoy the view for a moment before going inside.

CHAPTER FIVE

'The trivial round, the common task,
Would furnish all we ought to ask...'

When you walked in, there were two rooms, with a wooden partition between. The room to the right was the kitchen. The other room was where they all slept. Clemmie always had a narrow bed in a nook in the wall and it was almost like having a tiny room all to herself. She knew it wouldn't have been like that if she'd been living with her brothers and sister.

There was a big hearth for a fire in the kitchen and a smaller fireplace at the other end of the cottage, in the little bedroom. The walls were roughly plastered and lime-washed. In the window recesses and in some places along the walls, Uncle Walter had lined the granite with cabin doors from shipwrecks to keep out draughts and damp. The floor was made of planks of wood rescued from the sea, but there were stone slabs fronting the hearth. When she was an old lady, Clemmie was given a roll of linoleum to put down on the floor, but she left it propped against the wall.

'I do dearly love my wooden planks,' she used to say.

The kitchen was homely and crammed full of all the things needed to live comfortably. Wood for the fire was stacked almost as high as fern ricks in two piles near the hearth to dry out - stubs and driftwood in one pile, bracken and gorse prickles in the other. When they went gathering gorse, Uncle Walter used a little axe for chopping at the stubs and Clemmie helped by collecting them up in a big sack. After Walter and Betsy died, she always used Uncle Walter's little axe to collect her own stubs.

The chimney in the kitchen was huge. Walter's youngest brother (Sampson Pender Jenkins - always known as Uncle Sampy) used to say it was wide enough for a pony and cart to drive through and would laugh when Aunt Betsy complained that the flue was blocked and the fire wasn't drawing properly. To keep her happy Uncle Sampy would occasionally come round, climb up to the chimney and drop a rope down the flue. Walter tied a clump of gorse to the rope and then Sampy would pull it up. In this way they swept the chimney.

Even when she grew old, Clem liked the kitchen to be just as it was when she was a child. There was an old Cornish range on the end wall, but she had no use for it. She liked to heat up water and do her bit of cooking on the open fire. On the hearth stood all the pots and pans she needed and there was a metal plate, hinged to swing over the heat of the glowing stubs. Aunt Betsy had cooked using two large iron-kettles or pots; one was for baking bread and the other for boiling. Clemmie always kept them, but eventually they were too heavy for her to lift. They were curved at the base, with straight sides and a round open top. Each one had two small v-shaped handles for lifting. The dough was put in the pot to rise. As soon as it was ready, the whole pot was turned upside down and placed on the metal plate over the fire or on the hearth and covered with hot peat turf, so that the bread cooked inside. Therefore, the pot was called a kettle-oven. Her aunt used to bake barley loaves, but there was sometimes a wheaten loaf for special occasions. The loaves were always kept on a shelf in an alcove by the fire.

An iron, with its holder draped over the handle, stood in the hearth, ready to be warmed. The iron holder was the first thing Clemmie knitted when she went to school. On a washstand was a china jug with a bowl for washing and a small tin bath was propped against the wall beside it. There was a big wash-tub and an old wringer.

Once, a huge spinning wheel, almost as tall as a person, completely filled one corner of the room, but the spinning industry on Scilly gradually declined and the spinning wheel went after Aunt Betsy died It had originally belonged to Aunt Betsy's mother, Elizabeth, who used to live in the cottage. Clemmie never knew her, but Uncle Walter said she had been a schoolteacher and a spinner and he always gave the impression that Elizabeth had been quite a strong character. Aunt Betsy could be strict and she had very definite ideas about the way things should be done, so Clemmie always thought she must have got that from her mother.

The furniture in the cottage had come mostly from wrecks - a well-scrubbed table by the kitchen window and four upright wooden chairs. Uncle Walter made a simple dresser from salvaged wood, with shelves above and a table below. Always on this table Clemmie kept her uncle's big telescope, so important when the pilot cutters and gigs used to race to be the first to reach incoming ships or shipwrecks. Along the shelves stood blue and white plates, jugs and mugs, cups, saucers and bowls.

Clemmie knew that the picture on the biggest plate told a story. There was a willow tree, a man in a boat, three people on a bridge, a little island and two birds flying above. Uncle Walter told her that two of the people on the bridge were being chased by the third one. They escaped and were taken by boat to live on the little island. When their hiding place was eventually discovered, the gods turned them into birds so that they could fly safely away. Once, on Kitchen Porth, Clemmie found a tiny, worn fragment of pottery and on it were two blue birds. Uncle Walter told her it was the happy ending to the Willow Pattern story, so she always kept it as a symbol of happiness.

Up in the thatch by the fireplace, Clemmie kept all the bottles and jars she found on her shore-hunting expeditions. They were all shapes and sizes. Many were plain glass, but some were green, blue, brown and even red. In her later years, she took some of them to Henry Stedeford and he showed her how he could put little model sailing ships inside them. He also told her how he went out water divining with a forked twig. When there was water below the ground, the twig started twitching in his hands - or so he said. Clemmie tried it, but it didn't seem to work for her.

On its own shelf beside the dresser, the big Bible was always kept. Aunt Betsy plaited a straw cross to hang above it. Clemmie remembered being shown how to make a straw six-plait and the little rhyme she was taught to say,

"Under one and over two,
Pull it tight and that'll do."

She found it difficult enough plaiting with whole straws, so it would need great skill to weave the fine plaits used for making straw bonnets and baskets. For these, a special cutter was pulled through the straw to cut it into fine strips - sometimes as many as eight from one straw! To plait these neatly would require some practice.

Clemmie's childhood days at the cottage were busy and full. Aunt Betsy liked to keep to a strict routine, so certain things were done on certain days - for instance, not just on Shrove Tuesday, but every Tuesday, they cooked pancakes. Aunt Betsy told her that in the old days on Scilly the boys used to throw stones at people's front doors on Pancake Day and demand either a pancake or money.

'Those Jenkins or Pender boys better not try that with me,' she used to say *'or I'll give them what for!'* She would have, too.

The winding of the eight-day clock on the mantelshelf was another weekly ritual. Uncle Walter wound it up without fail every Sunday and it wouldn't do to be a minute or two late. The fire was always lit at the same time each day and throughout her life Clemmie hardly ever wavered from this. In fact, Bryher folk used to say that they didn't need to look at the clock, because they could tell the time from the smoke coming out of Clem's chimney.

When Aunt Betsy was alive and they had finished the cleaning, washing or bread making and prepared the cooked meal for the day - usually fish and potatoes - she would sit down with Clemmie and teach her how to sew, knit and crochet. From her aunt she also learned not only how to plait straw, but how to card sheep's wool ready for spinning.

Betsy taught her to enjoy gardening, too, and they spent many hours in their garden plot, digging up potatoes, pulling up carrots, picking flowers and gathering herbs. The sparrows and thrushes were as tame as could be, but Aunt Betsy shooed them away with her broom or by banging on a tray. She said they stole the reeds from the roof to build their nests and they would even roost in the thatch if she didn't keep them away.

'Get out, you little stinkers,' she used to shout.

In fact, she called them worse things than that, so it was just as well that the sparrows didn't understand exactly what she was saying. As a child, Clemmie was sad that her aunt drove the small birds away, for they were so tame and friendly they would eat from her outstretched hand. However, in later years, when she grew old and lived alone, she found herself behaving just like Aunt Betsy.

There was only candlelight in the cottage. In any case, Clemmie always liked to go to bed and get up with the sun. It meant that from October to February she got plenty of rest, but not so much in mid-summer. She felt safe lying in bed, listening to the ticking of the clocks. Aunt Betsy dearly loved clocks and so did Clemmie. Besides the one on the mantelshelf, there were several more in the cottage. They had all come from shipwrecks, but they seemed to work. Clemmie liked to watch and wait for the light from the Bishop Rock Lighthouse to beam through the window. Counting between flashes, she would quickly fall asleep.

They always lived very simply on Bryher. They didn't have a lot of money, but they were not poor. Most families kept a cow and hens, so there was an ample supply of milk and eggs. It was a good day when someone killed a pig and they could have some trotters. There were fish and potatoes aplenty and - though the preventive men did their utmost to stop it - tea, sugar, tobacco, wines, spirits and all kinds of fancy goods still filtered through to them, either as wreck salvage or from undercover bartering with crews of incoming ships. When there was no money to pay for things perhaps a bird or a rabbit would be accepted instead. The men were fishermen, farmers, boatmen - often all three. The women would spin, knit, sew, clean and cook and, both indoors and out, were true helpers of their men. It was this feeling that they were helping each other which made a hard existence not just endurable, but good. Life could be tough, but it was ordered and peaceful - and certainly never dull. The shipwrecks saw to that - and who knew what a wreck would wash ashore? Anything from coal to cotton to cattle to coconuts!

CHAPTER SIX

'And down, down went the Delaware...'

There wasn't a family on Bryher that did not boast a number of treasures salvaged from shipwrecks - but equally there were many shipwrecked sailors who spoke of the wonderful bravery and kindness shown by Scilly folk when their ships foundered on the fearsome rocks. Like all islanders, the people of Bryher loved a good wreck, where all lives were saved and useful cargo was there for the taking, but the saving of lives always came first. It might have been true, as some say, that in times of great hardship they prayed for wrecks to happen. However, it was not just for the cargo. A rescue also challenged their skills as seafarers and fulfilled their dreams of adventure and excitement.

The S.S. Delaware, bound for Calcutta from Liverpool, was wrecked just before Christmas in 1871. It didn't turn out to be a good wreck by Bryher standards, since only two out of fifty or so men on board were saved and most of the cargo washed ashore found its way to St. Mary's. Even though Clemmie was very young, she could remember shivering on top of Samson Hill that day and the sickening sense of fear and foreboding that gripped them all as they huddled together against the fury of the gale and screwed up their eyes to see what was happening out towards Mincarlo.

It had all happened a long time ago, but Aunt Betsy could relive it in detail for the rest of her life, so vividly was it etched on her mind.

'There could be no fishing that morning, Clemmie. The gale was screaming in from the west-north-west and the seas breaking on the Norrard Rocks were mountainous. Your Uncle Walter had gone to check on the pilot cutter A.Z., which had been safely moored in the shelter of New Grimsby Channel. He used to be master of the cutter and always fussed over that boat as if it were a baby.

We were cosy in our cottage, though. We had used stubs to make a fine fire and I had given you my box of buttons to play with, while I stood busy spinning. The wind was rattling the windows and gusting down the chimney, belching clouds of smoke into the little room. It drowned the whirr and creak of the huge wooden spinning wheel and the quiet ticking of the clock.

You were happily playing with the buttons, picking out all the pearl ones which were your favourites. Suddenly, above the roar of the wind, there were shouts and the sound of heavy feet pounding past. The door burst open and your Uncle Sampy cried 'Where's Walter? There's a ship in trouble between Seal Rock and Mincarlo!' He was gone before I could speak. Your uncle was fetched, Clemmie, but it was too late for him to join in the rescue. I think he suffered more than any of us, having to watch it all unfold, while he stood helpless on top of Samson Hill - but your Uncle Sampy went and we were all so proud of him and all the Bryher men that day.

I bundled you up in a huge shawl and we hurried as fast as we could to the top of Samson Hill. The ship, a big steamer, was drifting helplessly just to the north of Mincarlo. She did not seem to hit a rock, but suddenly three huge waves, one on top of another, capsized her. In no time at all she was smashed to pieces like matchwood and sank from sight.'

That was a moment Clemmie would never forget.

CHAPTER SEVEN

'Now may God bless those Bryher men...'

When the Delaware went down, all looked to be lost. Aunt Betsy took Clemmie home, but Uncle Sampy told them the rest of the amazing story many times and they never grew tired of hearing it.

'There seemed little hope that anyone could have survived and we looked in vain for any sign of life in the raging seas. Rescue seemed impossible. Our three cutters - A.Z., Rapid and the brand new Fortitude - were all anchored safely in the channel on the east side of Bryher. To sail westwards between Bryher and Samson against the full force of wind and waves would have meant certain disaster. We thought of launching one of our gigs - the Albion, berthed at the top of Great Par - but one look at the huge breakers told us it would be sheer madness to attempt to row from there around Droppy Nose

Point. All these thoughts were churning in our minds as we scanned the storm-tossed sea through telescopes.

Suddenly there was pointing and shouting as we spotted survivors - two men were seen clinging to half a lifeboat, two were clutching a spar and another hung onto a piece of wreckage. They were all being carried towards White Island. There had to be a way to save them. We put our heads together and came up with a plan. We would carry Albion half a mile overland to Rushy Bay and launch her there. If we could reach Samson safely, there was a chance we could get from there to White Island.

We rushed down the hill to the two gig sheds at Great Par. Albion was kept in one and March in the other. With the six oars lashed across Albion, twelve men each hooked an oar end over the crook of one arm and steadied the gig with the other. She was thirty feet long, with a beam of over five feet, and she weighed nearly half a ton. We staggered under her weight, but would not give up when there were lives to be saved. It was a relief to reach Rushy Bay and lower Albion into the water. Ten of us were chosen to carry out the rescue and, with Patrick

32

Trevellick as cox, we set out on the hardest journey of our lives. Rowing to Samson we had the wind and sea behind us, but slantwise from starboard, across the stern, so we needed all our strength and the gig creaked and groaned in the huge waves. At last we reached Samson landing beach and some of us jumped out and ran to the top of North Hill.

White Island lay about a quarter of a mile west and was being lashed by the fiercest seas I have ever seen. Through our telescopes we watched as the two men in the boat, each in turn, jumped as an incoming wave smashed them against the rocks and then scrambled ashore as the sea sucked back again. Sadly, however, the other three survivors, though they were washed onto rocks, had no strength left. They were swept away and never seen again.

We raced back to the gig. From the top of the hill it had been possible to see a way to rescue the two men now stranded on White Island. We could row Albion down to East Par beach and then carry her across land to West Par.

Rowing further down Samson in the lee of the land was relatively easy, but then began the gruelling task of carrying the heavy gig across the narrow neck between North and South Hill - only about two hundred yards it was, but the ground was rough and the storm against us. As we struggled over rocks and shingle, the cruel wind roared in our ears and whipped fine sand into our faces. We had to hang onto the thwarts of the Albion or the gale would have torn her from us. Worst of all was going over the slippery boulders at the top of West Par. If one of us had stumbled, the gig could have been damaged and our brave mission would have been over. It was a nightmare, but we kept going and at last reached the other side.

The plan was that Richard Ellis should stay on Samson to signal back to Bryher about our progress. That left nine of us in the gig - one cox, six rowers and two men to keep bailing out! Already exhausted, we now had to launch the gig into rough seas. It was only the sight of the two shipwrecked sailors clinging to rocks on White Island that kept us going, as, time after time, the crashing surf washed us back to shore.

*At last we were afloat and rowing as we'd never rowed before -
lunging forward, dipping oars and pulling harder at every
stroke.*

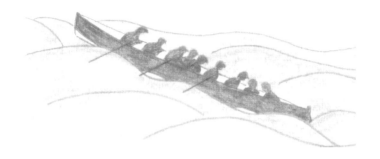

*Our muscles ached and our lungs were bursting, but Albion
served us well that day. Sometimes she was almost standing on
end in the huge rollers, but we kept her going, through the
seething sea, past floating bodies way beyond our help, until
we reached White Island. It was rocky there, but we had
already made a plan to stop the gig being smashed to pieces.
As we neared the shore, four of us jumped out, leaving five in
the boat to keep her safely afloat and waiting.*

*Now comes the part of the story beyond belief, because those
two poor, stranded souls, far from welcoming us with open
arms, waited defiantly on the shore ready to hurl granite*

pebbles at us. You see, they thought we were wild savages come to harm them. Imagine it - all that effort, only to be pelted with stones!

Luckily, they were far too weak to attack us and soon realised that we'd come to help and not hurt them. They were only half-clothed and shivering with shock and cold. We gave them our jackets, socks and a blanket and tended their gashed and bruised bodies as best we could. They were both too weary even to crawl, so we had to carry them to the Albion. The wind and waves were with us now and swept us safely back to Samson's shore.

From North Hill, Richard Ellis had already signalled back to Bryher for reinforcements. Albion's sister gig, the March, was carried over to Rushy Bay and launched to Samson. We left Albion on West Par and helped the survivors across Samson neck. On East Par we at last stopped to rest, sheltering the two shipwrecked men in a fern rick to keep them warm. Once the March arrived with dry clothes - well, the epic story of the Delaware was as good as over. We rowed the two men back to Bryher in the March and they were given hot drinks and warm beds in John Jenkins' house at Southard. The strange thing was that one of the rescued men - the Third Mate - was called Jenkins, like so many of us on Bryher.

Soon after the Delaware went down the shores of Samson were strewn with wood, bales of cotton, prints, velveteen and silks, but we didn't get to see much of that on Bryher. Our only reward was the saving of those two lives. Still, that meant a lot to us all. I can't remember using the Albion or the March again - I reckon they'd done their bit. Golden Eagle and then Czar were built to replace them. They were faster gigs and played their parts in later shipwrecks, but I don't think there could have been a braver tale than the one when we went to the rescue of the men on the Delaware. Only two were saved that day - two out of almost fifty - but with the weather like it was I don't think we could have done more.'

No-one could possibly argue with that.

CHAPTER EIGHT

Beads

Not long before she died, Clemmie's grandmother - Granny Martha Hicks - gave her a little leather drawstring bag of beads. Granny Martha had grown up on St. Agnes and she told Clemmie this story about the beads.

'One stormy morning, many long years ago, some folk on St. Agnes found the lifeless body of a sailor boy. He was lying in a small hollow at the foot of a high rock. On the shores of the bay they discovered wreckage and knew that there must have been a fearful shipwreck during the night. However, no other bodies were ever found. They supposed that the poor lad had somehow struggled safely to land and crawled as far away from the angry waves as his strength would allow. On reaching the shelter of the rock, he must have collapsed from sheer exhaustion and there he breathed his last. Ever since

that day, the place where the boy was found has always been known as Boy's Rock. Among the cargo of the wrecked ship was a large quantity of beads and, although all this happened some two hundred years ago, beads are still washed up by the tide in what is now called Beady Pool. Mind you, Clemmie, most of these beads were found, not in the sand or on the rocks at Beady Pool, but in ploughed potato fields. I think they must have come in with the seaweed carted up over the years.'

Some were like crystals and a few were black and white, oval-shaped and a reasonable size, but most of them were a terracotta colour, with a dull finish on the outside and dark glass inside. The terracotta ones were not very big. They were either barrel-shaped or straight and thin, like little tubes. Finally, there were dozens of small round beads, so tiny that even the finest needle would hardly go through the holes. These were perfect for making rings. When bad weather kept Clemmie indoors, she spent many happy hours arranging all the beads in different patterns and threading them onto a string of strong cotton to hang prettily round her neck. As soon as she had finished playing with them, she always pulled them off the cotton and counted them carefully back into the bag to make sure that none got lost.

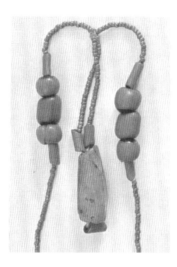

There was one bead which was different from all the others. Her grandmother had said it was cornelian agate. It looked like smoky glass and was a soft pink colour, tinged with a warm orange glow and streaked with veins of deep red. It was more than an inch long and had been cut into a shape rather like a long droplet. Granny Martha had found it in Beady Pool after a week of stormy weather. She had been clambering at low tide on the rocks below the shoreline when she saw the bead lying at the bottom of a shallow pool.

'The story goes that the beads were to be exchanged as part of the slave trade. The terracotta ones were not very showy, so some semi-precious and crystal beads had been sprinkled on top to trick the traders into thinking the cargo was more valuable. It may be that the agate bead was one of those - or it could be much older. No-one is really sure. There aren't so many like that one, Clemmie. You take good care of it.'

After Granny Martha died, Clemmie always had a strange feeling that she, too, would find something just as wonderful - and one day she did. It was a shiny, bright blue bead about the same size as the agate that her grandmother had found. Large and lozenge-shaped, it was cut like a precious gemstone, so that it caught the light and sparkled. She didn't need to search hard for it, because it was simply lying on the tideline at Popplestones, twinkling up at her in the sunshine. She picked it up delicately between her thumb and first finger and carefully placed it in the palm of her other hand. She stared at it in disbelief for quite some time. Then, with the bead tightly clenched in her hand for fear she might lose it, she hitched up her skirt and ran excitedly home to show Uncle Walter and Aunt Betsy.

'*Ah, now, I've seen some like this before,*' Uncle Walter said. '*Folks do say they're from a ship called the Douro, wrecked on Crebawethan some thirty years ago.*'

'*Well, I can't imagine how it fetched up here!*' Aunt Betsy cried. '*Washed ashore specially for you, I shouldn't wonder. Lord knows, you've spent time enough wanting and a-wishing for it.*'

Uncle Walter smiled and nodded his head.

'*Someone must be watching out for you, Clemmie,*' he said quietly.

Clemmie knew that finding something like that was rare and, although she always looked, she never really hoped to come across another one. Even the delicate pink cowries they called guinea moneys were hard to find on Bryher beaches. Most of Clemmie's had come from Tresco or Samson. Luckily, though, she could shore-hunt for other pretty trinkets on Bryher.

CHAPTER NINE

Mermaids' Tears

It was Mrs. James Jenkins who first told her about mermaids' tears. James and Mary Jenkins and their children lived in the White House at Norrard, a cottage perched up on the rocks, right beside New Grimsby Channel. Clemmie didn't often go to the northern end of Bryher, but Mrs. James had just had a little girl, Mary Sophia (a daughter, at last, after six sons!) and Aunt Betsy wanted to give her the fine bonnet she had crocheted for the new baby. Clemmie always enjoyed her rare visits to the White House. Although Mrs. James had one older brother, she often said how much she'd enjoyed her own company as a child. For that reason, Clemmie felt she understood her own quiet and independent nature.

It was the end of January, but a day 'God-given', with a pale sun shining from a mild blue sky and a gentle breeze blowing off the sea. Clemmie was dressed up for visiting, in best frock, straw-plait bonnet, boots and warm shawl. After they had admired the baby, Aunt Betsy settled herself down to talk and Clemmie wandered out onto Kitchen Porth to explore.

The beach here was enclosed and strewn with rocks. Below the tideline, the sand was stony and gritty. Everywhere she looked there were small fragments of glass, worn smooth and misty by the constant washing of waves and grinding of coarse shingle. She collected a few pieces in the palm of her hand and thought how pretty they were, with their delicate, muted shades - milky quartz, turquoise, jade, emerald, aquamarine and amber. They were like jewels that had lost their sparkle, but together they looked handsome.

After a while, she sat down and sorted through her precious hoard, selecting the very best ones to keep. Some of the pieces of glass were too big and some were still transparent, with sharp edges. These she threw back onto the sand. She put the rest into her hat and returned to the White House to show them to Mrs. James and Aunt Betsy.

'Oh, there you are, Clemmie! I was just thinking to come and find you. Time we went home,' Aunt Betsy said.

'What've you got there, Clem? Why, bless me, Betsy, if the child hasn't been collecting mermaids' tears! Just like me when I was her age.'

Mrs. James gave Clemmie a smile and a wink when she saw the puzzled look on her face.

'I always called them that. It made collecting them much more exciting,' she explained.

'Oh, Mary,' Aunt Betsy cried. *'Don't you go filling her head with any more nonsense!'*

But she was too late with her protests. The spellbound look on Clemmie's face must have told them both that she was completely captivated by this whimsical notion. After that, how could she ever imagine that those ocean pearls were anything other than the salty teardrops of lovelorn mermaids?

'Come on now, Betsy,' said Mrs. James. *'Let the child have some fun. I never did see any harm in a bit of wishing and dreaming. It gives life a touch of magic to fancy that deep down there are still mermaids. Isn't that right, Clem?'*

Clemmie nodded, then, after a quick glance at Aunt Betsy, looked down at the floor and shyly covered her mouth with one hand to hide her smile of delight.

When they got home, she found a crystal clear bottle and carefully dropped the mermaids' tears into it, one by one. They looked lovely inside the shining glass. The clouded whites, greens and blues reminded her of the ripples of the sea, while the faded brown fragments were exactly the colour of seaweed.

They were just as mermaids' tears should be and Clemmie dearly loved them.

CHAPTER TEN

'One is one and all alone...'

Bryher - 1875

Clemmie never knew whether she was happiest in her own company because she grew up like an only child, or whether it was in her nature to be solitary and self-sufficient - a bit of both probably. She loved being with grown-up people and listening to their talk, but, when they were busy, she would often wander off by herself rather than play with other children. Some people thought she was a strange little oddity.

She wasn't allowed to go up to Shipman Head Down by herself, for the cliffs around Hell Bay were dangerous and the seas often rough, but the south end of the island, from Popplestones right round to the beach by the church, was her kingdom. On fine days in spring, summer and autumn, she would go out exploring and could always find plenty to keep her happy.

Down by Great Par, near the gig sheds, the fishermen would spread out their nets to mend and she would often stop to help them. Uncle Walter had shown her how to hold the net taut, so that the knots she made did not slip - otherwise, he said, the fish would poke their noses through the holes and wriggle about till the holes grew bigger - and then they would escape and swim to freedom. Clemmie thought that mending a net was a bit like doing very large, loopy crochet - no hook, but her little fingers were nimble at making the knots.

As a child, she always liked the little sandy beach at the Gweal end of Popplestones. If she stood still in the shallows, little fish would come and swim around her feet. Sometimes she spotted the bright orange limbs of a starfish and watched as it buried itself in the sand.

Great Par, on the way to Heathy Hill, was a perfect place for treasure hunting. Here, she gathered up more mermaids' tears to add to her collection and it was on this shore that she found most of her ever-growing store of glass bottles and jars - all quite undamaged. She always hoped she might find a message inside a bottle, but there was never more than a little crab, which would scuttle out when it saw her.

Often she would climb her way to the top of Gweal or Samson Hill and look down at the land and sea below. The granite up there was weathered into curves and hollows and she liked to find the perfect nook to rest in, sheltered from the wind. From the top of Gweal Hill it was easy to see why Popplestones sometimes lay like a calm lagoon, its narrow neck keeping back the ocean beyond. It looked no distance from the two rope-thatched gig sheds to Rushy Bay, across the sandy strip of land that led out to Heathy Hill, yet it must have seemed an endless journey to the men who carried the gig on the day the Delaware went down. She could see the houses around Pool and on the road to Timmy's Hill. Almost at the top, outlined against the shining sea, were the roof and chimneys of Hillside, right next to their own little cottage.

From Samson Hill there was a wonderful view of boats coming up the channel from St. Mary's to Tresco and Bryher. Beyond Samson she could see St. Agnes, with its lighthouse clear against the sky. Yet somehow her gaze always came to rest on Samson's two hills and she could picture the Webbers and Woodcocks, who used to live there. Only twenty years or so before, the last few people left on Samson had reluctantly packed their belongings into a little boat and abandoned their island home. Now it was inhabited mainly by gulls, rats and black rabbits. Clemmie had been there on school picnics and seen the heaps of limpet shells outside the ruined cottages - evidence of the poverty and hunger the families had often endured.

Her great, great grandmother, Elizabeth Woodcock, had been born on Samson in 1743, but had come to Bryher when she married Thomas Jenkins. She used to tell her children that Christmas was always celebrated on January 6th on Samson, because that was the day that the sheep (blissfully unaware that in 1752 a new calendar had been introduced) fell on their knees to pray. Many of the thirty or so people called Jenkins who lived on Bryher when Clemmie was a child, were descendants of Thomas and Elizabeth.

Sitting on top of Samson Hill, surrounded by ancient burial chambers, it seemed natural to think about people who had lived on the islands long, long ago. It could feel quite eerie, though. When that happened, she knew it was time to pick her way carefully back towards Rushy Bay, through the bracken and gorse bushes.

Lower down and close to the sea were the two places Clemmie loved best of all - Heathy Hill and Wethers Carn. There were soft cushions of turf or thrift for her to sit on and stones to lean against or even to pillow her head. She liked to sit with her arms round her knees and watch the seals bobbing their silky heads out of the water. After a while, she would lie back and gaze into the distant blue above. It reminded her of the story of Jacob's Ladder in the Bible, when Jacob used a stone as a pillow, and she always thought how pleasant it must have been for Jacob to lie with his head on the stone and look up to heaven.

As she grew old, Clemmie didn't often feel like walking so far, but when she was in bed, before she went to sleep, she would take herself for an imaginary walk around Bryher and she could picture it all, just as it had been when she was a child.

CHAPTER ELEVEN

Simple Pleasures

If she ever felt in need of company, Clemmie would go looking for her brother Walter. It was Walter who taught her how to catch crabs with a hook and line, using fresh limpets as bait. It was an old tradition on Scilly to go limpeting on Good Friday, but Clemmie thought it must have been mostly for the fun of surprising the limpets before they glued themselves tightly to the rocks. Limpets may have kept the poor folk on Samson alive, but to her they looked like rubber and she didn't think any amount of cooking would have made them good to eat.

Anyway, after she and Walter had collected their bait, they would walk to the grassy mound by the landing beach, clamber down close to the gently lapping waves, squat precariously on the rocks and dangle their tempting hooks into the floating jungle of seaweed below. When she felt the familiar twitch,

Clemmie would haul up her line, release the surprised and desperately clawing crab and put it gently into her little bucket of water. They never caught crabs big enough to cook and eat, but the fun was feeling them nibble on the line, landing them successfully and seeing how many they could catch. Before sunset, they would return them all safely to the sea and walk happily home. At the top of the hill they went their separate ways. With a last wave from the brow of Timmy's Hill, Clemmie used to run down to her little cottage, suddenly aware that the hem of her dress was soaked with sea water.

Even when she was very small, she used to take off her boots, hitch up her skirt and go shrimping with Uncle Walter in the channel between Bryher and Tresco. When the tide was out they could walk right out to the sandbanks in the middle. The net was far too big for Clemmie to handle, so she used to stand by at the ready, while he eased and prodded the net under the clumps of seaweed. When he thought the cod end was full of shrimps, he let her poke it through and help the funny little grey shrimps into her bucket.

There was a big rock by the path leading down to Pool and here water used to collect after heavy spells of rain. In spring the water was full of frog spawn, so it was always known as 'Froggypool'. Clemmie loved to go there as a child and watch the tadpoles wriggling about. Almost every child on Bryher hoped to be first to see a little frog appear, so hardly a day went by when she did not visit Froggypool. Once she took some tadpoles home in a glass jar, but Aunt Betsy told her to take them straight back again.

'Clementina Hicks,' she began. Clemmie knew she was in trouble whenever she heard her full name spoken like that. *'We don't want frogs jumping all over the place. I've got enough to do, keeping those sparrows out of the thatch!'*

So that was that.

Clemmie couldn't remember having any toys as a child. She simply used things that came naturally to hand. At school, hopscotch and jackstones were popular games in the playground, using pebbles collected from the beach. In fact, her brothers found pebbles an endless form of amusement. She could remember how they used to build up a stack of small boulders at the water meadow end of Popplestones. Then they would throw pebbles and try to knock it down. Another time, they would place a pebble on the sand and, from a set distance and starting with four stones each, they would see who could throw one to land the nearest.

Both Henry and Walter were experts at skimming small flat pebbles or pieces of slate across the smooth water. Ducks and Drakes, they called it. Clemmie ran around collecting suitable pebbles for them to throw and then would hold her breath as she counted how many hops there would be before the stone finally sank beneath the surface. When she was by herself, Clemmie often tried to make the pebbles hop across the bay, but she didn't have the knack somehow. They always dropped straight into the sea with a dismal plop.

Granny Martha once took Henry and Walter across to St Agnes and showed them the maze of pebbles near Troy Town Farm. No-one was sure how long it had been there, but Granny Martha could remember running along its winding path when she was a child. The two boys tried to make their own maze on the sandy turf between Popplestones and Pool, but they had to give up. It was much harder than they thought.

Clemmie grew to cherish these happy memories of her childhood. However, there was work to be done as well, because all the children were expected to play their part in the life of the island. They also had to go to school.

Troy Town Maze – St. Agnes

CHAPTER TWELVE

School

Going to school in those days meant a daily boat trip across to Tresco and back, for there was no schoolhouse on Bryher then. Bryher did not get its own school until 1907. For Clemmie, the boat trip was the best bit of the day - but it was even better when they couldn't get to school at all, because of stormy weather or very low spring tides.

She would have been very happy to stay at home and Aunt Betsy would have been pleased to teach her, but the law was that all children should go to school. Even before the law, parents on Scilly weren't encouraged to keep their children at home. Augustus Smith, the Lord Proprietor, who used to live in Tresco Abbey, always said that it would cost a penny a week for Scillonian children to go to school and twopence if they didn't! So, whenever weather, tide, good health, potato digging or other essential duties allowed, about twenty children from Bryher were expected to make the short journey across New Grimsby Channel to school. Their attendance was never very good.

After the short boat trip, they walked across to Old Grimsby, past the church. During the years that Clemmie went to school, the old church was pulled down and the granite used to construct a new one, just a stone's throw to the east of the original building. The old wooden seats were taken out and refitted in the school.

Old Tresco Church – c 1870

The school is the distant building, extreme right

Tresco National School, as it was then rather impressively called, stood across the Green from the church, right beside the shining stretch of water between Tresco and St. Martin's. It was a substantial building, with room for around ninety children. On the days when all the Bryher children actually got to school, there would be about seventy pupils altogether. The Infants were taught separately from the older children.

Trapped inside its granite walls, Clemmie felt like some small, frightened creature in a cage. The benches were narrow and hard, the desks too high for her tiny frame. The fire smoked and the ventilation was poor. She could recall that one morning the schoolroom was so full of smoke that, to their great joy, they were all sent home. Many of the lessons seemed to have no meaning for her or the life she had grown to love outside the schoolroom. She was quiet and dutiful, but her spirits were subdued as her pencil tapped and scraped across her slate. While the children mechanically chanted facts learned by rote, her eyes would stray to the dust motes dancing in the sunbeams streaming down from the windows. She would picture the white beach outside and imagine herself there, scouring the sand for guinea moneys to take home to Bryher.

People say that education has a way of killing imagination and certainly much of what Clemmie was taught at school seemed dull and pointless. However, some lessons served to fuel her fanciful way of looking at things.

Needlework and poetry were her great favourites. Aunt Betsy had encouraged her in all kinds of handwork long before she went to school and it was a pleasure for her to feel needle, thread and cloth in her hands. While others clumsily struggled over samplers or garments all crumpled, frayed and grubby, her nimble fingers fairly flew over the fabric and she was praised for her fine and neat stitches. And while she sewed, she could also daydream.

She was quick to learn poetry, too. Many children hated the task of memorising and reciting passages of verse, but Clemmie loved rhymes and rhythms and the vivid pictures that poems conjured up in her mind.

One poem she heard at school and always remembered was 'The Pied Piper of Hamelin'. At the north end of Tresco was a cave known as Piper's Hole.

Clemmie had been there with her big sister and brothers. To reach it you had to climb carefully down from the grassy cliff top to the rock-strewn gully below. The entrance was small and uninviting, for you had to bend double and scramble over large granite boulders, worn smooth by the constant pounding of the waves that broke in at high tide. Then the tunnel opened out into a lofty cavern and you could stand upright. There was a deep, still pool of fresh water on which a small boat was kept in summer, so you could ferry across and land on the little beach at the far end of the cave. Many legends and stories were told about it, but Clemmie dreamed up her own picture. She imagined a piper, clothed half in yellow and half in red, like the Pied Piper in the poem, emerging from the dark cavern, with the band of children skipping behind him, for Scilly was their promised land, the paradise that beckoned brightly. But when she told Uncle Walter he just laughed and said,

'Well, if the piper did all that, Clemmie, why can't he rid Scilly of the dreaded rats?'

And they both laughed, so perhaps school wasn't **all** bad! Clemmie never told Aunt Betsy her foolish fantasy. She would have thought it was nothing but silly nonsense.

When Clemmie was about six, a ship was wrecked at Peninnis Head on St. Mary's in thick fog, for there was no lighthouse at Peninnis then. She was a four-masted barque from Peru, bound for Dublin and carrying a cargo of guano.

Half her crew drowned, but the rest escaped before help arrived by scrambling up the jib-boom and shinning down a rope onto the headland, so there was no dramatic rescue - and no rush to plunder the cargo of fertilizer! However, the name of the ship, together with the lines of poetry the children heard and recited at school after she was wrecked, fired Clemmie's imagination. She was called Minnehaha and, because of her, Clemmie was introduced to 'The Song of Hiawatha'.

The Minnehaha, Peninnis, 1874

She wasn't the only one to be inspired by this poem. All the children collected gulls' feathers for Red Indian headdresses and her brothers, Henry and Walter, made bows and arrows, shot them in the air and raced after them, sparked off by the lines:

"He could shoot an arrow from him,

And run forward with such fleetness

That the arrow fell behind him!"

What Clemmie did not know then was that thirty-six years later, by the strangest coincidence, a second ship called Minnehaha would be stranded on Scilly's shores - and she would be carrying a cargo beyond their wildest dreams.

CHAPTER THIRTEEN

'All things bright and beautiful...'

After school the children would land on Bryher beach and on most days Clemmie walked with her brothers up the winding path beside the church to the top of the hill. Here they would part. Henry, Walter and William would go on their way to join the rest of the family in their bustling, crowded house in the Town, while she went home alone. Her sister Sarah-Jane and her eldest brother Stephen had left school by then and her youngest brother, Thomas Albert, was still too young for lessons.

The way back to Sparrow Cottage lay in the opposite direction. After a short climb, the path curved to the right and began to drop down to skirt the south side of Timmy's Hill. At this point, Clemmie would stop and gaze in wonder. She could never have analysed or put into words the reasons for her overwhelming sense of happiness, but it was not surprising that the scene before her always took her breath away.

The whole of the southern part of the island, from The Brow right round to Great Par, was set out before her like a picture-map. However, it would not have been the details of the landscape that gave her that sudden surge of joy, but the amazing feeling of space and the intensity of light and colour. The expanse of sky and sea was immense, so that the first impression was of a blue radiance everywhere.

Gradually her eyes would take in all the soft green hues of the island - greens mixed with blues, greys, pale browns and yellows. Soon, other images would begin to emerge: hills, yellow with flowering gorse or rust red with dying bracken, gentle slopes of purple heather; the delicate greens of grasses on sand dunes; cottages roofed with slate or light brown reed thatch; warm granite, twinkling with crystals and encrusted with pale grey-green or golden lichen; undergrowth flecked with wild flowers; white sand and the blue, incredibly blue, shining ocean. Out to the west, silhouetted against the light and washed by breaking waves, were the familiar dark shapes of the big rocks with fairy tale names - Mincarlo and Castle Bryher - and way out on the horizon stood the Bishop Rock Lighthouse.

The shades of the sea in the channel between Bryher and Tresco would be beyond belief - sparkling sapphire, often splintered with silver sunlight, green and turquoise in the shallows over sandbanks and deep blue turning to purple where rocks and seaweed lurked below. It was a vivid picture, yet so tranquil - for the natural colours all merged happily together.

Aunt Betsy would sometimes be working in the garden when Clemmie got home from school. It was to the east side of the cottage and caught the sun all day. Flowers, herbs and vegetables grew in haphazard fashion, but there was no plant that did not flourish under her tender love and care. She never went visiting without picking a bunch of flowers or filling a basket with vegetables to take as a gift - a habit that she passed on to Clemmie. Her favourite flowers were the deep crimson gladioli the islanders called 'whistling jacks' - 'jacks' because they looked like small flags fluttering on a flagpole and 'whistling' because when you pressed the sword-shaped leaves between your palms and blew, they made a whistling sound.

As Clemmie grew up, she saw important changes taking place on Bryher. It was always beautiful - its natural setting made sure of that - but when she was younger there had been mostly brown potato fields and bare drystone hedges around gardens and farms. Land that had not been cleared and cultivated was usually overrun with brambles and bracken. However, after she left school, the flower industry began to prosper and many men who had earned a simple living from piloting or fishing became flower farmers instead. A patchwork of fields - small 'squares' cleverly pieced together on every available sheltered slope above the shoreline and edged with newly planted protective fences - gleamed in sunlit strips of white and gold. The silver-backed, dark olive leaves of pittosporum and the glossy greens of veronica and escallonia began to appear, acting as both backdrop and framework to row upon row of flowers. From February to April the air was filled with an almost overwhelming scent of daffodils and narcissi.

The influence of Tresco Abbey Gardens could also be seen everywhere. In fact, it was often difficult to decide where gardens ended and natural vegetation began, for there were exotic plants wherever you looked: mesembryanthemums draped themselves over granite hedges and sprawled across the sand dunes; fleshy aeoniums, like small inflated cabbages, their flowers like turrets of gold filigree, seemed to spring from nowhere in a twisting tangle of rope-like stems; graceful purple echiums arched upwards like skyrockets and agapanthuses, tall and majestic, proudly displayed their crowns of brilliant blue flowers. These were originally brought to Tresco Gardens by Augustus Smith, but it was not long before they took root and flourished all over Scilly. Then there were geraniums, tree mallows, and fuchsias, which climbed as high as the eaves and spilled over the grey cottage walls in cascades of shimmering colours.

A stranger might think that winter days were dull and dreary, that bad weather brought an eerie sense of uneasy isolation, but the islanders were used to the mists swirling in and the ferocious Atlantic storms, whipping the waves into a fury and hurtling with full force against everything in sight. It was all a part of life on Bryher, so they simply got on with what they could, took each day as it came and waited for the sun to come out again.

Anyway, Clemmie always felt safe and contented living with Uncle Walter and Aunt Betsy, even though Aunt Betsy could be quite sharp sometimes. They were kind, hard-working, God-fearing folk. She did not envy her sister and brothers and she was sure they did not envy her. Their parents' decision to give Clemmie away meant that her life could never follow the same pattern as theirs. Yet they were all happy enough. In those early, carefree days of childhood, none of them could know that their destinies would be so tragically different because of that decision.

CHAPTER FOURTEEN

'All creatures great and small...'

Clemmie's Grandfather Jenkins - Granfer Thomas - died when she was nearly nine years old, but because Uncle Sampy worked with him, he was able to look after his five acres of land until he grew old. Clemmie could remember him clearly, because she spent a lot of time with him, helping with the farm animals. It was Granfer Thomas who showed her how to milk a cow and let her gather up the eggs, which the hens managed to lay in all kinds of unexpected places! And like a lot of old folk on Bryher, he liked to talk.

'When I was a young lad, all the cattle on Scilly were small and black - not like the handsome cross-breeds and Jerseys we have now. Many of the winter bullocks were fed on potatoes and a little dry meat, but they also ate a lot of seaweed. Still, you couldn't taste it in their meat. Lovely it was - much richer

and a better flavour than nowadays. Not like the pigs. They ate seaweed, too, but you could taste it when you killed a pig for Christmas.

But the funniest story about animal feed affecting flavour is this one, Clemmie. A ship called the Sado fetched up on Gorregan in the Western Rocks with a cargo of wool, wine and oranges. It happened a year or more before the Delaware was wrecked, so you'd have been too young to remember. For weeks we were all eating oranges and the hens ate the peel. Well, I shall never forget the taste of those hens' eggs, with their fine flavour of oranges. How we all laughed!'

Clemmie said it would have been even funnier if the eggshells had turned orange as well, but apparently they hadn't. She really missed Granfer Thomas when he died, but it was good that Uncle Sampy was happy to carry on farming the land.

There were more sheep on Bryher then, grazing on any available piece of open ground, but they were bred to provide wool for the spinners rather than for their meat. Their loose, shining wool was usually plucked rather than clipped and then it would be washed, dyed and carded, ready to be spun into fine yarn for the knitters.

The 'cards' were pieces of flat wood with hooked wire teeth on one side and wooden handles on the back. One card was drawn across the other two or three times and the teeth acted like a comb to straighten out the tangled fibres. Finally, with a light curling action, using the reverse of one of the cards, the carder produced a long, fluffy roll which could be drawn out and twisted into a continuous thread by the spinner. Aunt Betsy often recalled the long winter evenings, when she and her mother used to card and spin wool by the flickering firelight. However, as the flower industry began to prosper, less and less spinning was done on Bryher, so there was not so much call for sheep.

But they still made good use of their small horses and donkeys. Clemmie used to wonder how these animals managed to eat the prickly gorse, until she watched them one day and saw them carefully using their front hooves to bruise the leaves before eating them.

Whilst Granfer Thomas encouraged her to love and care for farm animals, it was Uncle Walter who took her out in his boat and taught her to enjoy the sea birds and seals. Aunt Betsy wasn't very fond of boats and, if sparrows and frogs were anything to go by, she certainly didn't like birds or water creatures. However, when a fine, calm afternoon came along, Uncle Walter and Clemmie would set off together for the Norrard Rocks.

They would sail out from Great Par and make their way westwards towards Maiden Bower. Clemmie liked it when she was allowed to take the tiller. She had no difficulty in knowing port from starboard, but Uncle Walter made her laugh when he told her about one poor lady who never knew t'other from which. The story got about that her husband tied a bucket on one side of the boat and a broom on the other. After that he could shout simple commands like 'Hard a'bucket' or 'Hard a'broom'. Apparently it worked a treat.

They would nose the boat gently in and out between Maiden Bower, Seal Rock and Illiswilgig, looking for grey seals. It was best when the tide was low and the lazy creatures seemed to be sunning themselves on the exposed rocks. They always appeared to be just as curious about humans as humans were about them, but when the boat came too close they would lollop awkwardly down the rocks to the water's edge and slide gently into the sea. If one went in, it wasn't long before the rest followed. However, their heads soon bobbed up above the surface as they kept a friendly, watchful eye on the boat. In early autumn Clemmie sometimes spotted the creamy white fur of a seal pup, which had been safely born well above high water. After three weeks it would be deserted by its mother and have to fend for itself. She hoped it would survive.

April, May and June were the best months to see puffins. Most of them nested on Annet, near St. Agnes, but there were usually plenty to be found around Mincarlo. With their small wings, they made hard work of taking off and landing, though they were very quick to watch in flight. Underwater, they beat their wings to swim along at great speed. Clemmie liked it when they caught sight of one sitting plumply upright on a rock with a neat row of sand eels clenched in its colourful beak. Those comical beaks also acted as perfect shovels for scooping out the underground burrows where they laid their eggs. Uncle

Walter explained that a puffin laid only one egg, so it needed to be safe from scavenging black-backed gulls and other predatory creatures. By mid-July most of the puffins had gone, for they spent the winter far out to sea - well away from the inquisitive eyes of birdwatchers and their telescopes.

The other birds they both enjoyed watching were the gannets. Gannets were the biggest of the sea birds, with a wing span of six feet. They were white with black wing-tips and Clemmie usually spotted them cruising high above a patch of open sea. Sometimes they would hunt in pairs, but there could be quite a group of them. They appeared to be gliding idly above the water, but really their hungry eyes were on the constant look-out for any sign of fish below. Suddenly, one would fold back its wings and dive, streamlined, from a great height. At high speed, straight as an arrow, it would plunge into the sea with a spectacular splash to capture its prey in its cruel beak, way down in the depths below. It was so exciting to watch, especially when there was a whole crowd of them diving one after another.

They also saw cormorants and shags, razorbills and guillemots, terns, oystercatchers, fulmars and kittiwakes and all kinds of gulls, but Clemmie always thought it was an especially good afternoon's sailing when they saw seals, puffins and gannets. However, what could really crown the day was the sight of a school of porpoises playfully wheeling in graceful arcs alongside their boat as they sailed home in the sunset.

They never did see any mermaids, but not for one moment did Clemmie stop imagining that they were still there, deep down.

CHAPTER FIFTEEN

Bryher Baptist Chapel

There had been a little Church on Bryher since 1742, but the original one, a simple rectangular building with no tower, was even smaller than the cottage where Clemmie lived. Since then All Saints' Church had been rebuilt and enlarged to allow more people to worship there. It was well attended for christenings, weddings and funerals, but for regular services it was not so successful. Just one service a week was held there, conducted by a visiting clergyman from Tresco. Many a time this could not take place because of low tides or stormy weather. Some families on Bryher felt they wanted to be more independent and that worship should reflect their spirit of simplicity and freedom. It was this need for more spiritual fellowship that led a group of islanders to meet together for worship in Richard Hicks's cottage, which stood barely fifty yards from Clemmie's home, on the corner of the track leading down to Southard Green.

The Old Meeting House
Richard Hicks's Cottage

Clemmie often thought about those early meetings. While the adults gathered in the tiny bedroom-parlour of the cottage for prayer and praise, the children stayed in the kitchen with Richard's wife, Mary-Ann. On a Sunday morning, Mary-Ann Hicks would be busy cooking for the Sabbath dinner and the children must have got in her way and under her feet, but she never complained. Clemmie was just six or seven years old then, but she could remember those happy times in Mary-Ann's kitchen.

What started as a simple prayer meeting grew into a definite order of service, with prayers, Bible readings and hymns. As there was no piano or organ, Uncle Walter always led the singing. Clemmie felt so proud, standing in the kitchen and listening to his fine, booming voice. Mary-Ann gave the children tasks to do, but they loved to join in the hymns as they worked.

As the simple prayer meetings prospered, it wasn't long before they began to wish for a Chapel of their own. The perfect place for it seemed to be near an outcrop of rocks known as Broomyfield, at the top of the track which wound its way up from the Church - the place that Clemmie and her brothers always called 'the parting of the ways.' It would be right beside the path leading to the Town and command wonderful views of the landing beach and channel on one side, with Pool, Gweal and the Norrard Rocks beyond on the other. Furthermore, it would be a fairly equal walking distance for all those who wished to come.

Building work started in September 1876 and it was all finished by the following June. The materials were given as gifts by those in the fellowship. The granite for the walls was quarried on Bryher and huge planks washed ashore by the sea provided more than enough wood. The pews were made from pitch pine salvaged from shipwrecks.

Over twelve pounds was paid to a St. Mary's builder for the walls to be built by contract, but Aunt Betsy was heard to remark that the Bryher men did most of the work while he supervised. They worked like Trojans to get the Chapel finished and the women helped them with any practical task that they were able to do. Even the elderly Charlotte Stideford was seen holding a straight rule against the newly plastered wall so that the plasterer could rule it off in squares. The children were eager to help as well and stood by, ready to fetch and carry tools, stones, wood, water or whatever was needed.

At last came the day when the Chapel was opened and the islanders gathered together to pray and sing in a house of worship they had built with their own hands. After the service there was a special tea. Uncle Sampy and young Charlotte James Stideford had been married only a few days before, so their new tea set was put to good use and everyone was given a piece of their wedding cake. It was such a wonderful day!

Of course, they had asked the new Governor, Thomas Algernon Dorrien Smith, for permission to build the Chapel. This had been given, on condition that the Chapel services were not held at the same time as those in the Church.

'And I suppose the next thing you want, be a Methody Parson!' the Governor is reported to have said.

In fact, they did not need a preacher. Richard Ellis, a Trinity Pilot, led the service with his fine, expressive voice. On

Sunday morning there was a simple prayer meeting, but in the evening he read from the published sermons of Charles Haddon Spurgeon, which were preached at the Tabernacle in London. Each sermon gave the numbers of the hymns and the scripture readings to be used and these were followed to the letter. Clemmie especially liked the Psalms and the Song of Solomon, but the reading she loved best was the story of St. Paul's shipwreck, ending with the words 'They escaped all safe to land.' That meant a lot to them all.

For the rest of her life Clemmie could picture Richard Ellis as he stood in the pulpit to preach, with the printed sermon held in one hand and a candle in the other. One of her treasured possessions was the brass candlestick he held while delivering the sermon at evening service. He was loved by all the children on Bryher and his Sunday School was always very lively.

The Chapel was well built and cared for. Those who had helped to build it saw it as a labour of love to keep it clean and in good repair. At the harvest festival it always looked especially beautiful. Wreaths of belladonna lilies bedecked the walls, the window sills were laden with fruit and vegetables and a sheaf of corn rested in front of the pulpit.

Inside Bryher Baptist Chapel

Clemmie always wondered if they were given divine guidance to build the Chapel, for soon after it was finished Mary-Ann died and Richard Hicks, who was blind, went to live with Richard and Sophia Ellis. When the flower industry began to flourish, the Hicks's little cottage, where this venture had all begun, was used as a bulb store and packing place. Nowadays it is the Bryher blacksmith's forge.

Uncle Walter continued to lead the singing for many years, until he grew too old and weak to go to Chapel any more. Then, with no one to fill his place, an instrument was acquired - an American organ. It came to Bryher like a gift from heaven.

CHAPTER SIXTEEN

The Sycamore Tree

While Clemmie was still at school, her parents, with her sister and five brothers, left Bryher and went to live on Tresco. Her father, Patrick, was over sixty - nearly twenty years older than her mother. With the decline in piloting, he was no longer able to look after his big family just by farming and fishing. The four youngest boys still went to school, but the two eldest children, Sarah-Jane and Stephen, both living at home, were grown up and in need of work. It was a sad day for Clemmie when she watched them pack all their belongings into the boat and sail across to Tresco. Her mother, Mary-Jane, was secretly heart-broken to leave Bryher. She felt she was abandoning Clemmie for the second time. Clemmie longed to say the right words and comfort her, but somehow her mother had never encouraged any closeness between them. Clemmie's place was with Uncle Walter and Aunt Betsy. Mary-Jane never once wavered from that.

They went to a cottage below the Block House and Patrick worked as a gardener at the Abbey. Sarah Jane and Stephen became apprentice millers and butchers. Clemmie found it strange coming home from school without her brothers and, even though she was always happy in her own company, she still missed them, especially her favourite brother, Walter.

It wasn't long after she left school that her brother Henry died. He was only twenty-one and had been working as a groom and domestic servant before he became ill. At first, Aunt Betsy told Clemmie he had a bad cough, but it did not get better and within a year he had died of tuberculosis. Oh, how Clemmie came to dread that word! Seven months later, Sarah Jane, aged thirty, was also dead.

However, the tragedy which proved hardest of all to bear came at the end of 1885 when Walter was drowned. Like Henry, he was just twenty-one. He went wrecking one day - going aboard a wreck to see if there was anything he could salvage. Whilst he was on the wreck, the ship lurched, he was trapped and he drowned. Clemmie could remember exactly what she had said to Uncle Walter by way of comfort.

'But I suppose if he'd have lived, he'd have died.'

He knew just what she meant - if the sea had not taken young Walter, he would almost certainly have died of tuberculosis anyway - but it would have sounded very odd to a stranger.

Henry, Sarah-Jane and Walter were all buried in the same grave in St. Nicholas' churchyard, on the west side of the new Church, which had been completely rebuilt only six years before Walter was drowned. 'The Lord hath need of them' were the brave words inscribed on their gravestone. Clemmie was only seventeen, but suddenly life became uncertain and she began to value everything more dearly. Unbelievably, further sorrow was yet to come.

William died next. He was just eighteen, nearly two years younger than Clemmie. Grass had barely grown over his grave when Stephen died. He was not yet thirty. 'Home with Jesus' were the comforting words chosen for their headstone, but their parents were inconsolable. They had lost five of their children in the space of six years. Mary-Jane suffered more than anyone; she saw it as some kind of punishment for farming Clemmie out as a baby - something she was now to regret until she died. Clemmie could only hope that one day her mother would discover what a wonderful gift she had bestowed on her younger daughter - a long and contented life on Bryher - for while Mary-Jane was alive Clemmie could never find the words to tell her.

Life continued in the little cottage on Bryher, but those were dark days and Clemmie would never have got through them without the steady love and faith surrounding her. Her uncle and aunt kept her spirit strong and everyone on Bryher was there to comfort her, but she couldn't help wondering what would have happened to her if she had gone with her family to live in the cottage near the Block House. It was more than likely that she would have been dead, too. Everyone had this strange feeling that somehow Clemmie had been spared and Uncle Walter kept repeating the words she had so often heard before,

'Someone must be watching out for you, Clemmie.'

Her mother only lived for another four years. She was fifty-six when she died in 1892. Thomas Albert, Clemmie's one surviving brother and the youngest of them all, lived until 1901. Aged twenty-seven, he was the only one who had married and he left a wife, Helen, and two little girls. Patrick Hicks lived to be eighty seven, but died a year later. So they were all gone - but Clemmie never forgot them.

The gravestones of Patrick and Mary-Jane Hicks

Near the porch of her cottage Clemmie planted a sycamore tree which was very important to her, though it also filled her with an uneasy sense of guilt. You see, she took the little sycamore sapling from Tresco and brought it home with her. It was the only sycamore on Bryher and it grew and flourished into quite a handsome tree. When there was a south-easterly gale it gave some shelter from the full force of the wind and on a hot day it offered some shade. Clemmie loved this tree, but Aunt Betsy always thought it attracted even more birds to their cottage and, if she had got her way, it would have been chopped down. However, Uncle Walter always understood why the tree meant so much to Clemmie and it stood in front of her cottage for the rest of her long life, reminding her of a happy afternoon she spent on Tresco with her family, soon after they had all gone to live there. I believe it is still there now.

Clemmie often thought about them all, but she was not one to stand at graves and mourn. She tried to make the most of her own life, believing that was the best way to remember and honour those who were no longer with her. She hoped they had all found peace, for she thought that their lives must have been harder than hers.

CHAPTER SEVENTEEN

Aunt Charlotte

Aunt Betsy did not like talking about the past very much. She was always too busy living in the present. So whenever Clemmie wanted to hear about olden times, she would go to see Aunt Charlotte.

Charlotte Stideford was Uncle Sampy's mother-in-law. She was a well-known Bryher character and was affectionately known as Aunt Charlotte to everyone, for it was the custom in Scilly to call the older, respected members of the community aunt or uncle, whether you were related to them or not. She must have been about sixty when her daughter, also Charlotte, married Uncle Sampy. Her husband, James, had been a Trinity Pilot, but he had been drowned the year Clemmie was born. A lady who visited Bryher painted a picture of Aunt Charlotte. The painting was printed in a book about Scilly, but Clemmie wasn't sure if Aunt Charlotte ever lived to see it. Everyone thought it was a wonderful likeness of the old lady. She is sitting outside on a wooden chair, with a red shawl around her shoulders and wearing a grey cloth bonnet, which ties under her chin and drapes over the back of her neck. She was certainly the oldest inhabitant on Bryher then and she was ninety-six when she died.

'The Oldest Inhabitant'
Painting by Jessie Mothersole
1910

She had a sharp little face and piercing eyes, but her whole face seemed to smile and twinkle as she talked. She loved to tell Clemmie all about her life as a little girl growing up on Bryher and she would sew or knit as she talked. In fact, she had been a tailoress and her daughter, Charlotte, was a dressmaker. Both of them made the most beautiful clothes - shirts, blouses, skirts, dresses, coats and hats, all neatly sewn by hand.

Clemmie was good at sewing and knitting, but at school they were taught dull, practical things like darning, run-and-fell seaming, sewing on buttons, making buttonholes, patching and gathering. So far she had only managed to make a roller towel, a pillow slip and a linen apron. She had knitted an iron holder, a duster, a child's vest and a stocking, using three needles to turn the heel. When she looked at all the lovely garments that Aunt Charlotte and her daughter had made, she wanted to be just as neat and clever. Sometimes she took some crochet work she had done and Aunt Charlotte helped and encouraged her to try even harder. Eventually she was able to do the finest crochet imaginable and there was nothing she liked better than making exquisite bookmarks and collars to repay people for their kindness.

As she grew older, Aunt Charlotte would relate the stories she had already told many times before, but Clemmie never grew tired of hearing them.

'Did I ever tell you about the time when some stockings were knitted in Scilly and sent to the king?' she used to ask.

And Clemmie would always say no and settle down to hear the story once more.

'I was only a baby, but my mother was so proud of this story she kept telling me about it. It was just before George the Fourth became king. I believe he was known as the Prince Regent. The off-islands were going through a time of great poverty and, to provide work for the poor islanders, some spinning wheels had been given to them by the School of Industry. The Prince Regent was a patron of this organisation and by way of thanking him it was decided that two pairs of lambswool stockings should be sent as a present. So the stockings were knitted - on St. Martin's I think it was - and the initials GPR, surrounded by a fanciful wreath, were embroidered on each one in crimson silk. They were thought

to be the finest stockings ever made and very hard-wearing! They were placed in a mahogany box and sent to the Prince Regent and I believe a letter of thanks was received from London.'

Clemmie knew Aunt Charlotte would not stop there. She loved thinking back to her childhood, even though it was a time of such great hardship and endurance.

'That was a terrible time for the islanders, Clem, when I was a girl. It was the last years of the kelp industry. At low tide all through the summer, day after day, men, women and children would be cutting the ore-weed and dragging it up the beach in baskets or on sledges. Each family had its own piece of ground where the weed could be spread out and raked over until it was thoroughly dry. Then they would burn the weed in the kelp-pits and the fires would be burning well into the night. The smoke hung everywhere in a great cloud. Doors and windows had to be barred to keep out the smell, but even so it got into our clothes and furniture and lingered long after the summer was over. Next morning the solid mass of kelp from the burnt ore-weed was broken up into handy lumps and stored until mid-

August. Then it was all shipped to Bristol to make glass and soap. No more than £5 a ton was paid for it and, with twenty-four tons of seaweed needed to produce one ton of kelp, it was hard work for small reward. Most of us thought it a blessing when there was no longer a market for kelp.

Burning seaweed for kelp

Another venture introduced to change our fortunes at that time was a mackerel and pilchard fishery. Fish cellars were built on Tresco, and we were provided with several boats, completely fitted out with mullet nets, trammels and long lines. But that idea didn't last long - a couple of years maybe. A bit too ambitious for our simple way of life, I dare say. Still, people here used to eat a lot of salted fish. 'Scads and taties all the week and conger pie on Sundays' was always a familiar saying on Scilly. It was certainly true once, but the Salt Tax weighed heavily on the poor islanders and this meant that less fish could be preserved for the winter months.

After that, the shipbuilding industry began. Wooden ships were built on St. Mary's to take surplus produce (mainly potatoes) to the Mediterranean and they brought back cargoes of fruit to England. Then there has always been the piloting and, of course, the shipwrecks. But I'm afraid that's all dying out now - too much steam, too many lighthouses, not to mention the spoiling tactics of the preventive officers. The coming of the iron steamships brought an end to the shipbuilding as well. Yet even in times of great distress we never forgot how to enjoy ourselves, Clem. On St. Mary's, especially, many of the old customs were still celebrated.

At Christmas time there was goose dancing. Nothing to do with geese at all! The name came from the old French word 'guise' - meaning to dress up as someone else. The islanders disguised themselves by blackening their faces or wearing strange masks. *They dressed up in every kind of old garment you can think of - women dressed as men and men dressed as women - and paraded through Hugh Town carrying turnip lanterns.*

On May Day, a tall pole from the shipbuilding yards would be set up on the Parade. Gorse petals were collected and scattered all about and the maypole was bedecked with wreaths of leaves and flowers. There was a May Queen and throughout the day children danced around the maypole.

The next big celebration took place on Midsummer-eve. When it grew dark there were bonfires and crackers. Tar barrels were set alight and the young men brought gasps from the assembled throng by swinging lighted torches around their heads. I did hear tell that the blazing tar barrels were then sent rolling through the streets of St. Mary's.

Hardly any corn is grown in Scilly these days, but not so long ago it was mostly corn and potatoes that kept us alive. Harvest time and the gathering-in of the corn was celebrated with a 'Nikla Thies' party at the 'House of the Mow'. After a meal, there was dancing all night until daylight. But, sadly, we don't seem to keep up these traditions any more. I think the children on St. Mary's still dance on May Day, but the other customs have died out now.

Oh, there was feasting and dancing on Bryher as well, Clem, and we still know how to celebrate christenings and weddings, don't we? Always a feast or a famine in Scilly, eh? But there aren't enough young girls on the island now to do the dances we used to do. There was one dance I remember called Phoebe. It was mostly skipping, but there was a step called 'footing it'. You hopped on each foot alternately and on each hop you tapped on the ground with the heel of your other foot. There were four heel taps - right, left, right, left - before you skipped around to turn your first corner. Then the whole step was repeated with your second corner. I loved doing that - and the 'Phibbie', as we called it, had such a pretty tune.'

Sitting on her chair, Aunt Charlotte would lift her skirt above her ankles and show Clemmie how to do the step, tapping each heel down in turn and then skipping on her toes in time to the song she sang:

"Cannot you dance the Phoebe,

Don't you see how my shoulders shake,

Don't you see what pains I take,

Cannot you dance the Phoebe?"

'I do wish you could have danced that at Sampy and Charlotte's wedding, but there were only three little girls on Bryher about your age. You need six to make up a set and somehow the boys didn't take kindly to dancing, did they Clem?' she said, her eyes twinkling with merriment.

They both laughed as they pictured how the boys would have fallen over their own feet if they had tried to 'foot it'.

'There have been some changes in Scilly in my lifetime and I've seen bad times and good. But something always seems to turn up! Someone must be watching out for us, Clem.'

And Clemmie used to smile, because that was what Uncle Walter always said about her.

CHAPTER EIGHTEEN

'Consider the lilies of the field …'

'Something'll turn up,' Aunt Charlotte kept saying.

She said it when the shipbuilding on St. Mary's finally finished, and again when the early potato crop failed.

Well, the lilies didn't exactly turn up - they were there all the time. They had been growing in Scilly as long as anyone could remember - not in any organised way of course, but randomly, on cliffs, in unploughed fields and along the grassy fringes of sea-washed shores. That's what the islanders always called them - lilies. No-one really knew where they had come from. Some said that the monks of the old St. Nicholas Abbey on Tresco must have planted them, but Uncle Walter thought it was much more likely that they had been washed ashore from one of the many Dutch shipwrecks or had come to Scilly through the age-old Scillonian custom of bartering with foreign ships; that before this practice was eventually outlawed by the preventive officers, bulbs were exchanged for corn, vegetables and other fresh produce and planted haphazardly around the islands. Clemmie's favourite story was that the first bulbs were given to the wife of a governor of Star Castle by a Dutch Merchant Captain. She thought they were onions and boiled some. When she came to eat one, it tasted so horrible that she picked up all the rest and threw them into the dry moat around the Castle. Of course, they grew and flourished, as plants have a habit of doing when you take little trouble over them.

No, it wasn't the flowers that turned up. It was the idea that there might be a market for them.

'What a pity you didn't discover this gold mine earlier,' visitors often said.

In fact, it wasn't <u>there</u> earlier. Though the lilies had been flowering in Scilly for years, there would have been no value in trying to sell them. It was only when there was an increasing demand for cut flowers from ordinary people for their own homes that the market became prosperous and profitable. And it was by some lucky chance, at exactly the right moment, that Mr William Trevellick of Rocky Hill, St. Mary's, packed some bunches of lilies in a hat box and sent them to Covent Garden Market. The money he received for them made him realise that, even allowing for freight and transport costs, flowers could change Scillonian fortunes. 'Aunt Ellen's Hat Box' as it came to be called was to transform the islanders' lives.

No-one is quite sure of the exact year it all began, but Clemmie remembered that soon after she had finished school every available patch of sunny land on Bryher became a hotchpotch of small flower 'pieces' and natural shelter belts were newly planted to protect them. These fields, sometimes only a few square yards in size, huddled side by side, competing for each inch of ground away from damaging winds. Everyone, it seemed, was growing flowers. Uncle Sampy was already a farmer, with four acres of land, and it wasn't long before Uncle Walter, by then nearly sixty, also realised that there was a better living to be made from the land than from fishing. Flower-houses with big windows to let in the sunlight seemed to spring up overnight. Here the picked flowers were bunched and tied, ready to be carefully packed in the wooden boxes specially made from sawn timber sent from Scandinavia.

The lilies, which came to be known as Scilly Whites, were a kind of narcissus with more than one flower growing on each stem and it was these, together with Soleil D'Ors - Sols as they were always called - which were mainly grown to begin with. Then there were Grand Monarques, Pheasant Eyes and the Yellow Daffodil. However, the heavily-scented Sols were always the mainstay. They hated any frost, so would not thrive anywhere but Scilly and in the Channel Islands.

At first the season began soon after Christmas, but as competition grew it seemed to get earlier and earlier. However, the harvest reached its peak from February through to March. During this time the children were given three or four weeks holiday from school to help, so the whole island was caught up in a frenzy of flowers. The boys worked with the men out in the fields, nipping the stalks off with their fingers and placing their handfuls of flowers in deep mawn baskets. It could be bitterly cold and on wet days they needed leggings to protect themselves from the long, dripping wet leaves. In fine weather, the women and girls sometimes asked if they could help in the fields, but Clemmie was always happy to stay in the warmth of the flower-house, where they all laughed and talked together as they worked. They put the flowers in pots and made sure the petals had dried out thoroughly before bunching.

There were twelve blooms in each bunch. They were arranged so that they did not crush each other and then the stems were tied together with raffia, which had already been cut by the girls to the right length. It was amazing how quickly the flowers were bunched. Some said that women on St. Mary's could tie more than a thousand bunches in a day. Many developed a skin irritation called 'lily rash' caused by the sap from the stems, but this didn't hinder them in their ceaseless activity.

By late afternoon the flower-house was a wonderful sight, with banks of flowers arranged row upon row. Their perfume was overwhelming. They were carefully counted and packed in their shallow wooden boxes, each containing three, five or six dozen bunches. The tap-tap of a hammer could often be heard well into the night as the lids were nailed on to make them ready for the steamer next morning. In the early morning light, the boxes were stacked high in the Bryher boats and transported down to St Mary's Quay on the first stage of their journey to market.

You can imagine how the islanders dreaded winter frost, damaging winds or a thick fog which delayed the sailing of the steamer. Any of these could ruin their flower harvest. No season was the same. Sometimes flowers came early, sometimes late and sometimes they came all at once in a rush and were wasted, because they could not be picked and sent to market fast enough.

People thought it was an easy way to make money, but it was never that. In the summer months, after the harvest was over, the farmers were kept very busy transplanting, clearing the ground and trimming the shelters. It was back-breaking work. The bulbs needed to be lifted and divided every few years, although the Scilly Whites could be left in the same place for twenty years without appearing to take any harm. The dead leaves were raked off and used as cattle fodder. At first they were used for litter, but the cows ate them with great gusto, even though the green leaves would have been poison to them. So that was why lily ricks were seen side-by-side with hay ricks all over the islands.

'It might be hard work, Clem,' Aunt Charlotte said, *'but it gives us a living and flowers are much better than kelp.'*

Clemmie often wondered what would have happened if the flowers hadn't come along, but no doubt something else would have turned up!

CHAPTER NINETEEN

The Bishop

One of Clemmie's earliest memories was of lying in bed at night and waiting for the beam of the Bishop Rock Lighthouse to shine through the window of the cottage. Because it had always been part of her young life, she didn't really think about how it had got there or ever worry that it might be gone after the next big storm. But Uncle Walter never felt like that about the Bishop. You see, he could remember when the first tower was washed away.

'It was an iron structure, Clemmie. Cast iron pillars were sunk into the granite rock and braced with wrought iron rods. This outer framework surrounded and supported a central column which would house the keepers and give access to the lantern. The idea was that the waves could roll freely through, but also be checked by the foundations. It was thought that in this way

the slender column in the middle would not have a continuous
fight against the full force of the sea.

THE BISHOP ROCK
LIGHTHOUSE

The Iron Tower
1849

After two years of fairly slow progress and several setbacks,
the framework and the living apartment were all finished, but
with winter coming it was decided to wait until the following
spring before putting the lantern and its apparatus in place.

During the winter there were several bad gales, but it was in February 1850 that the worst storm arose. I always remember the date, because it was just about the time that Betsy and I were married. The storm raged all night and in the morning nothing was left of the iron structure except the bottom ends of the iron pillars. The only good thing to be said is that the gale came then, before the lighthouse was finished and there were men living on it.

However, the builders and engineers refused to give up. You see, the Western Rocks were a terrible danger to ships and were still without a light. St. Agnes was our only lighthouse then and its beam didn't shine far enough to warn ships approaching from the south-west. New plans were drawn up and this time the tower on Bishop Rock was to be round and built of granite.

A start was made on this project only a year after the first tower had been destroyed, but the wonder to me, Clemmie, is that they ever got started at all. It wasn't like building Round Island, where the men could land and remain in safety once they were there. No, on the Bishop they had to work from a

113

boat that would have been bobbing about all the time, completely at the mercy of the sea and the weather. Then in order that the base of the tower should have the biggest diameter possible, they had to lay granite blocks <u>below</u> the low water mark. These were actually put in place after some higher blocks had already been built, but even so it needed a master engineer to make sure all the pieces fitted together. Furthermore, until the tower was big enough to house the men working on it, everything had to be left at the end of each day until they could return. They used the exposed nearby island of Rosevear as a base and there must have been many a time when they prayed that all their hard work would not disappear overnight.

Progress was painfully slow. No building could be done over the winter months and it took a whole year to lay the base. The men had great difficulty in landing the stones brought to the rock in barges, which were towed down from the work yard on St. Mary's. Even after they had got the tower nearly up to its intended height, they were still experiencing all kinds of setbacks. However, in 1858, after seven long years, the tower was finished and the light shone out.'

And that was the light which shone through the window of the cottage every night. As a child, Clemmie always took it for granted. However, Uncle Walter still fretted about the Bishop. After a bad storm, he would stand at the front of the house and look long and hard down to the south-west through his telescope.

'Just making sure she's still safe, Clemmie,' he used to say.

He was quite right to worry. He had heard that during bad weather the whole tower shook and things inside were thrown all over the place. In one very bad storm the fog bell, which weighed five cwt and was fixed a hundred feet above high water level, was torn from its bracket and washed away, together with a flagstaff and ladder lashed to the gallery. Parts of the lantern were cracked and later it was discovered that some of the outer granite blocks a few feet above high water were split because of the enormous strain being put on the whole tower. The engineers decided to strengthen the lighthouse from top to bottom by bolting heavy iron ties to the walls inside and connecting them through the floors, but after another violent storm, there was further damage to the blocks just above high water.

By 1882 yet more plans had been made; the whole of the base and most of the existing tower were to be encased in another layer of granite, the blocks all being dovetailed together so that they could not pull apart. The walls would then be more than three feet thick! At the top, two extra storeys would be added, so that the lighthouse would be some forty feet higher and the light visible from a greater distance. The fog signal was to be a guncotton explosion instead of a bell.

The granite was quarried in Cornwall, but much of it was cut and fitted together on Rat Island, St. Mary's, before being shipped down to the Bishop in the steam vessel, Hercules. As before, the difficulties came with handling the huge blocks, any of which could weigh up to three and a half tons, and winching them into position. Then it could take two men - a mason and a hammerman working together - up to two days to prepare each new block for dovetailing. Although there were often as many as thirty men working on the rock, it still took far longer than would have been the case with a completely new building.

Nevertheless, in 1887, after five years, the work was finally finished. In all that time there was no loss of life or serious injury and the light continued to shine.

Working on the Bishop
1882 - 1887

It was in the same year that everyone on Bryher climbed up Watch Hill and first saw the comforting red light winking from Round Island, north of Tresco. But putting a light <u>there</u> was an easy task compared with the building of the Bishop. The white lighthouse stands on a big, flat-topped rock a hundred and thirty-six feet high, well away from the full force of rough seas.

The keepers said that the Bishop still swayed in a storm, but Uncle Walter did not need to worry any more that it would fall down. On every clear night its light beamed on Clemmie, as it had always done, but now she never took it for granted. She liked to think of the three keepers, lying in beds that were curved to fit the circular walls of their home. She wondered if they sometimes felt lonely and afraid out there, but she thought probably not. She believed they must feel proud and pleased to live in a lighthouse.

CHAPTER TWENTY

The Sewing Machine

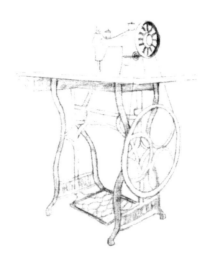

It was several years after the Bishop was finally finished that Clemmie first saw a sewing machine. It was certainly after her twentieth birthday.

On Bryher they had never really known a machine of any kind. Everything was done by hand and took a great deal of time and effort. So you can imagine the amazement when they were shown the wonders of a sewing machine.

Clemmie could remember that day so clearly. There was great excitement on Bryher, because the travelling draper's shop had arrived in a barge, towed from St. Mary's by the steam launch. Everything had to be unloaded, piled high onto a cart and taken up to Uncle Sampy's flower-house in the Town. Here, all was carefully unpacked and spread out on display beneath the vine leaves and climbing roses. The glass-house looked as colourful as it did at the height of the flower season, but instead of the masses of narcissi and daffodils, there was an array of goods brighter than anyone could ever imagine: rolls of white calico, blue linen and scarlet flannel, straw hats of every colour of the rainbow, satin and velvet ribbons in a multitude of widths and shades, delicate lace and frillings, silks and cottons, bootlaces and threads, shiny buckles, beads and buttons, needles and pins, tape measures, silver thimbles and scissors, stockings and socks, gloves, blouses and babies' bonnets, even toys for the children! And in the midst of all this - a wonder to behold - stood the sewing machine.

It was mounted on a wooden table which had wrought iron supports. Between these there was a treadle of latticed metal on which you rocked your feet to keep the machine going. At the side of the right-hand support there was a big wheel. The machine itself shone with new paint of black and gold. It consisted of two uprights joined by a bridge across the top. Two reels of cotton were held in place on small spool posts at each end of the bridge. On the right side was a wheel with a shining rim, much smaller than the one below, but attached to it by a loop of wire cable which threaded through the table-top. On the left upright were various hooks and gadgets through which the cotton was threaded before it reached the needle. This was held at the base of the upright in a vertical position, with the eye at the bottom. There was a little silver foot surrounding the needle, which clicked down to hold the fabric firmly in place. Underneath, there was a row of metal teeth called the feed dog, which moved to and fro and pushed the material along as you sewed. But the really clever thing and what made it so quick and neat and strong was that there was a second thread below, which interlocked with the thread from the needle on top to make the stitches and seam the material together.

An agent had come specially to show them how it all worked. Using the machine, he wound some thread onto a small circular bobbin. This fitted neatly inside a shuttle, which was then clipped into place below the needle. He then guided the top cotton down, around a little wheel and through a series of hooks and eyes, before threading the needle. Finally he snapped the foot down onto the cloth and set the machine in motion. Clemmie stood, quite speechless with astonishment.

With his feet working the treadle, he kept the big wheel turning. The top wheel whirred, the cotton reel spun and the needle thrummed rapidly up and down, galloping at speed along the material. In next to no time, the machine had sewn the firmest, neatest, straightest line of stitches Clemmie had ever seen. Aunt Charlotte spoke for everyone.

'My dear life,' she exclaimed. *'I did never think I should live to see such a thing!'*

From that day on, Clemmie secretly dreamed of having a sewing machine of her very own.

CHAPTER TWENTY-ONE

Pipe dreams

Sadly, as young people grow up, the burdens of everyday life have a nasty habit of getting in the way of dreams. In spite of this, Clemmie never gave up hope of having her own sewing machine. She knew it would happen one day and she was quite happy to wait. You couldn't hustle the tide in and out or force the wind to change direction. Dear me, no. She remembered how her longed-for special bead had suddenly twinkled up at her that day on Popplestones, as she always knew it would. She had the same feeling about the sewing machine, though she wasn't sure exactly when or how it would come. After all, a sewing machine was somewhat bigger than a little bead! However, there was no harm in wishing and dreaming, Clemmie reminded herself. She never once thought that she might be wishing for the impossible. When life became humdrum and seemed in danger of losing its magic, she would smile and whisper to herself,

'Don't forget! Deep down there are still mermaids.'

As long as she could keep imagining that, Clemmie thought, then anything was possible. She also had great faith that one day they would be getting the organ they were all wanting for the Chapel.

By Clemmie's fortieth birthday, Uncle Walter and Aunt Betsy were both in their eighties. They had always cared for her and now it was her turn to look after them. Uncle Walter, especially, was growing very frail and the day came when he could no longer go to Chapel. He had led the hymn singing for thirty years and suddenly, without his fine, strong voice, their songs of praise sounded weak and thin. There was no one to take his place.

'What we really need is an organ,' said Uncle Sampy's sons, young Sampson and Ernie.

'What we really need is an organ'

Everyone agreed with them, yet no one did anything about it. The general feeling was that if God wanted them to have an organ, then He'd make sure to send them one. So that was another dream waiting to come true.

'Don't you worry, Clem. Something'll turn up,' Aunt Charlotte said, as usual. So Clemmie didn't worry.

On the eleventh of November 1909, Uncle Walter died. He was eighty-three. It's strange, the silly little things people remember about funerals. After the service at the Chapel, the coffin was carried to the churchyard, where it was to be buried in Granfer Thomas's grave. It was such a sad and solemn occasion, yet the detail Clemmie recalled most vividly was the difficulty the bearers had in manoeuvring the coffin out of the Chapel. She supposed when it was built, no one thought about funerals. They obviously did not foresee the awkwardness of carrying a coffin down some steps and then turning sharp left to go out through the door at the side. However, the tricky moment added a human touch and she was sure Uncle Walter would have enjoyed it. He was a great one for seeing the funny side of things.

Clemmie always regretted that he didn't live just a little bit longer, because he would have been quite astonished at what happened next.

CHAPTER TWENTY-TWO

Shipwreck!

There hadn't really been any significant wrecks off Bryher since 1899, when a German ship, Erik Rickmers, carrying a cargo of rice, struck Scilly Rock in dense fog. Her crew of twenty-six were rescued by Bryher boats before she sank. A few hours later the French three-masted barque, Parame, also struck Scilly Rock and became a total loss, though her crew of ten were also saved. She was carrying a cargo of coconuts! It seemed that thick fog and Scilly Rock could be a deadly combination for ships trying to navigate their way safely past the islands - and so it proved in the early hours of April, 18th 1910.

The night it happened the islands were shrouded in fog. There was no fog signal on Round Island then, but on Bryher could be heard the boom of the gun fired every two minutes by the

Bishop. As usual, Clemmie had gone to bed early, but she couldn't get to sleep for the distant moaning of steamers' whistles as they crept past the Scillies. Just before midnight she kept hearing a much deeper hoot from the north-west. It seemed to get louder and louder. Then there were voices outside the cottage and the sound of footsteps hurrying past. She thought she recognised John Jacob Jenkins and his two sons and they seemed to be talking about going up to Hell Bay. She must have fallen asleep then, for the next thing she knew was being awakened by an urgent shout and a knock on the door. She ran outside to find the whole island in an uproar. There were no men to be seen - they had all rushed off to launch the gigs. 'A wreck,' was all the women knew and the three gigs were on their way. The men had disappeared so fast you would have thought they had all gone to bed fully dressed and ready for a rescue!

The Czar and Golden Eagle were launched from Great Par and the Sussex from the east side of Bryher. They didn't need to search for the wreck, because John Jacob had already reported that it had gone aground on Scilly Rock. The men in the Sussex got there first and were amazed to find a huge four-masted, single-funnelled liner, quietly resting with her bows on the rock and her stern still afloat. Her name was Minnehaha and she had been on her way to London from New York.

Her sixty or so passengers were leaning over the rails, gazing down on the ship's boats already moored alongside. As soon as the Czar and Golden Eagle arrived on the scene, all three gigs hailed and the cox of the Sussex, Richard Thomas Jenkins, was invited up to the chartroom to show the captain exactly where Minnehaha was wrecked. After this, the passengers were helped into the lifeboats, which were then towed to Great Par by the Czar and the Golden Eagle. By the time the St. Mary's lifeboat arrived, the passengers had all been taken off.

Once safely on Bryher's shores, the poor shipwrecked people were shared out amongst the houses and taken home to hot drinks and warm beds. The Sussex stayed all night by the wreck, keeping watch, but fortunately there was no big sea running and Scilly Rock acted as a breakwater. It looked as though Minnehaha would stay exactly where she was for some time.

The Minnehaha aground on Scilly Rock, April 1910

CHAPTER TWENTY-THREE

'Just what we wanted'

The next morning Bryher was a sight to behold. The island was buzzing like a hive of bees and the rescued people were all standing about with red blankets around their shoulders to protect them from the chill breeze. Across each blanket, in big black letters, were the words 'Atlantic Transport Co.' Of course, none of the children had gone to school and a group of them were gathered spellbound around one of the passengers. Later the children reported that all his teeth were made of gold and every time he laughed a gold mine sparkled in his mouth. Bryher children had never seen anything like that before.

However, arrangements were soon made for the passengers to be sent on their way, and then all thoughts turned to the Minnehaha and what was to be done with her and her cargo. Experts believed that there was a reasonable chance of floating the ship off, but first - oh joy - most of her cargo would have to be taken off to lighten her. Included in her general cargo were three hundred cattle. The first task was to get these ashore safely.

The poor creatures were pitched into the sea one by one, in sets of six, from a height of about thirty feet. They were lashed, three each side of each gig, and then were half-swum, half-towed, to Samson. It was back-breaking work, but nearly all were landed alive and well. They were later transported by cattle boat to the mainland.

Once the cattle were safe, orders were given to jettison all cargo from the forward holds. Such a sight was then seen on Bryher as had never been witnessed before! Hell Bay was littered with everything under the sun: casks of oil and fat, huge barrels of leaf tobacco, cases of Old Judge cigarettes, Panama hats, bundles of pens and pencils, hundreds of clocks, pill boxes by the thousand, wringers, washing machines, cash registers, dress lengths, wheels, typewriters, phonographs, sewing machines, boxes of jewellery, crates of Californian oranges and barrels of apples, even a motor car, a grand piano and a harp - and, unbelievably, washed up in the Bight, a consignment of harmoniums being shipped to the Aeolian Hall in London.

Vessels of all kinds converged on the island - tugs, salvage steamers, fishing boats and at least one small steam coaster appeared, hoping for a job lightening the ship. Boats from every island joined in the work. Each morning the regular gig crews would go out to see what was floating around. They never knew what would turn up next. One day it was bags of flour and they finished the day wet through and covered with dough! Another day it was hundreds of heavy casks, which had to be parbuckled aboard - a tricky job which could easily dip the gunwale of a lightly built gig. The 'potting dandies' were called in to help, with four men in a boat to parbuckle the casks aboard. Every shore and par was lined with casks, all rolled up above the high water mark.

Boatloads of men, women and children arrived daily from the other islands. Bryher was swarming with sightseers and shore-hunters and every other person, from five to ninety-five, seemed to be smoking Old Judge cigarettes!

They were busy on board the 'Minnie' as well. Her steam was kept up to work the pumps and stop the water reaching her fires. In the cookhouse, larder and bakery, the crew worked hard keeping the salvage men supplied with food, including lovely fresh bread every day.

Salvaging went on for three weeks, until the weary crews could do no more. Then, on the evening of May 10th, the tugs took up their positions to attempt to pull the liner off the rocks. With the Minnehaha's powerful engines going astern, they twisted and struggled, but she was stuck fast. Divers were sent down to find out why she didn't move and they found a torn plate hooked down into the rocks. They cut it free and next day, at high tide, after half an hour of pulling, the Minnehaha was afloat. With some sadness everyone watched her being escorted round to Crow Sound, where she anchored before eventually leaving Scilly for Southampton. The best bit of wrecking that Bryher had ever known was over.

The Minnehaha – afloat again after three weeks

But that wasn't quite the end of the story. The casks and any pieces of salvage still on Bryher had to be shipped to St. Mary's Quay and placed in the care of Lloyds agents. The two flower boats, 'Genesta' and 'Boy Ned' were rigged out to hoist the casks aboard and as soon as a full cargo was stowed below, they set sail for St. Mary's. This went on until all the casks were safely handed over. But human nature being what it is, by no means all the 'Minnie's' cargo found its way to St. Mary's.

One sunny day a few weeks later, Uncle Sampy came over with the donkey cart, so that Clemmie could take Aunt Betsy to visit Aunt Charlotte. Of course, the two old ladies talked of nothing but the wreck, each trying to outdo the other with the tales she had heard. The excitement of it all would long outlive them both.

On the way home, as they passed the Chapel, Uncle Sampy turned to Clemmie with a smile.

'It looks as if we might be getting an American organ for the Chapel, Clem.' He gave her a big wink.

'Really?' she answered with a knowing smile. *'That's good, then. Just what we wanted!'*

On the brow of Timmy's Hill they met young Sampson and Ernie, wheeling one of the wooden carts used for carrying boxes of flowers. They stood back with a cheery wave to let the donkey cart pass and gave the thumbs up sign to Uncle Sampy.

When they reached the cottage, Aunt Betsy and Uncle Sampy stopped outside to look at the view, but Clemmie turned towards the door to go in and light the fire, ready to put the kettle on. A seagull was standing on the roof of the porch. As it flew off, a white feather fluttered down and landed right in front of her feet. She bent down to pick it up, before going inside.

The sewing machine stood right in the middle of the kitchen. It even had a red bow tied on it. Clemmie stared at it in disbelief for quite some time. Then she went closer and reached out a hand to touch it, just to make sure it was really there. It must have come from the wreck of the Minnehaha, but she couldn't imagine how it had fetched up in their kitchen.

Aunt Betsy had come in quietly and was watching from the doorway. She spoke the words more gently this time, but Clemmie recognised the echo from the past.

'Washed ashore specially for you, I shouldn't wonder. Lord knows, you've spent time enough wanting and a-wishing for it.'

And she remembered what Uncle Walter always used to say:

'Someone must be watching out for you, Clemmie.'

She felt both happy and sad at the same time. There was a familiar pricking of tears in her eyes and a lump in her throat, as a huge rush of emotion welled up inside her. She had always tried to stay strong and hide her feelings. Through all the bad times Clemmie had never once cried, but now she buried her face in her hands and wept with joy.

How she wished her Uncle Walter could have been there. But she liked to think that perhaps he knew all about it anyway.

*   *   *

138

EPILOGUE

After the death of Aunt Betsy in January 1913, aged eighty-four, Clemmie lived at Sparrow Cottage alone. Her cousins Sampson and Ernie always kept a watchful eye on her and in the early 1950s, when Clemmie became too frail to manage alone, she was cared for by Ernie and his wife, Vi, in their newly-built bungalow, Pera. She died in 1953 and was buried in Bryher Churchyard. The inscription on her simple gravestone reads:

In ever loving memory of

CLEMENTINA HICKS

who died August 4th 1953

aged 85 years

At rest

*   *   *

ACKNOWLEDGEMENTS

I should like to thank Paul and Ruth Jenkins, Richard Jenkins, Peter and Sheila Miller, John Pender, Ted Langdon, Rosalie and Mike Tildesley, from Bryher; Arthur Jenkins, now living on St. Mary's and the late Rene Darling, formerly of Bryher, Tresco and St. Mary's, all of whom provided valuable first-hand information about Clem, her cottage and the Old Meeting House; Mary Jenkins of Bryher for articles from The Scillonian Magazines; David and Kathy Stedeford for the photograph of Clem; the Rev. Douglas Sparkes and the Rev. Philip Gathercole, former Baptist preachers on Bryher, for their memories of Clem and the copy of my father's sketch of Bryher Chapel; Helen Musser for dance instructions and music for 'Phoebe'; Amanda Martin, curator of the Isles of Scilly Museum, for access to Tresco School Log Books and information on beads, shipwrecks and sewing machines; The Cornwall Centre, Redruth, for access to Censuses and a multitude of reference books; the Superintendent Registrar, Isles of Scilly, for copies of Birth and Death Certificates; and last, but by no means least, historian, Michael Tangye, for pointing my research in the right direction on so many occasions.

Paintings of Clem's Cottage (Cover and Frontispiece) and Bryher Chapel are by Arthur W. Gay.

The following pictures are copies of photographs taken by the Gibson family, St. Mary's, Isles of Scilly, who have given kind permission for them to be included in this book:

Thatched Cottage on Bryher
Bryher 1875
Beads from St. Agnes
The Old Church, Tresco, c1870
The wreck of the Minnehaha, Peninnis, 1874
Burning seaweed for kelp
The wreck of the Minnehaha, Scilly Rock, 1910
The refloating of the Minnehaha

I am indebted to The Scillonian Magazine for invaluable accounts of straw rope spinning and plaiting (L.A. Hayward), the building of the Bishop Rock Lighthouse (Trevellick Moyle) and the wreck of the Minnehaha in 1910 (E.R. Jenkins). I have also gained a wealth of information and inspiration from the following authors and books:

Robert Heath - The Isles of Scilly. 1750.

J.C. and R.W. Tonkin - Guide to the Isles of Scilly. 1882.

J.G. Uren - Scilly and the Scillonians. 1907.

Jessie Mothersole - The Isles of Scilly. 1910.

A. and H. Gibson - The Isles of Scilly. 1932.

R.N. Shaw - Bryher Baptist Chapel. 1937.

E.L. Bowley - The Fortunate Islands. 1945.

Clive Mumford - Portrait of the Isles of Scilly. 1967.

Robert Maybee, The Scillonian Poet - I.O.S. Museum. 1973.

Richard Larn - Cornish Shipwrecks. 1973.

A.J. Jenkins - Gigs and Cutters of the Isles of Scilly. 1975.

Geoffrey Grigson - The Scilly Isles. 1977.

Charles Thomas - Portrait of a Drowned Landscape. 1985.

Penny Gay